Vocabulary
in Context

FOR THE COMMON CORE STANDARDS

Grade
6

Table of Contents

Introduction 4
Determining Meaning Through Word Analysis
  Prefixes 5
  Suffixes 6
  Roots and Word Families 7

Unit 1
A Vanishing Breed 8
Context Clues 10
Word Maze 12
Standardized Test Practice 13
Multiple-Meaning Words 14
Understanding Related Words 15
The Latin Prefix *dis-* 16
Writing 17

Unit 2
Annie Dodge Wauneka 18
Context Clues 20
Word Maze 22
Standardized Test Practice 23
Understanding Related Words 24
Understanding Multiple-Meaning Words 25
True or False 25
The Latin Roots *socius* and *bene* 26
Dictionary Skills 27
Writing 27

Unit 3
How the Sun Came 28
Understanding Figurative Language 30
Context Clues 31
Crossword Puzzle 33
Standardized Test Practice 34
Synonyms and Antonyms 35
Dictionary Skills 35
Understanding Multiple-Meaning Words 36
Word Meaning 36
Writing 37

Unit 4
The Black Hole 38
Context Clues 40
Word Maze 42
Standardized Test Practice 43
Understanding Multiple-Meaning Words 44
Understanding Related Words 45
The Latin Prefixes *ex-* and *pro-* 46
Writing 47

Unit 5
The Dogholes 48
Context Clues 50
Crossword Puzzle 52
Standardized Test Practice 53
Understanding Multiple-Meaning Words 54
Understanding Related Words 55
The Greek Word *techné* 56
Writing 57

Unit 6
Gold! 58
Context Clues 59
Word Groups 59
Word Origins 60
Cloze Paragraph 60
Word Riddle 61
Yes or No? 62
Standardized Test Practice 63
True or False 64
Questions and Answers 65
Suffix *-ful* 66
Latin Root *duct* 66
Writing 67

Unit 7

A Man of Vision 68
Context Clues 69
Word Maze 70
Tangled-Up Words 71
Standardized Test Practice 72
Understanding Multiple-Meaning Words 74
Synonyms 75
The Suffix *-ion* 76
Word Pairs 76
Writing 77

Unit 8

Faces in Stone 78
Context Clues 79
Word Groups 80
Analogies 80
Crossword Puzzle 81
Yes or No? 82
Standardized Test Practice 83
True or False 84
Synonyms 85
The Prefix *pro-* 86
Writing 87

Unit 9

For the Glory of Zeus 88
Context Clues 89
Word Map 90
Connotations 91
Find the Word 91
Word Maze 92
Analogies 93
Cloze Paragraph 93
Standardized Test Practice 94
Understanding Related Words 95
Challenge Yourself 95
Word Groups 96
Rewriting Sentences 96
Writing 97

Unit 10

Wall of Wonder 98
Context Clues 99
Word Map 100
Find the Word 101
Crossword Puzzle 102
Analogies 103
Cloze Paragraph 103
Standardized Test Practice 104
Using Context 105
Word Sense 106
Understanding Multiple-Meaning Words ...106
Writing 107

Glossary 108

Answer Key 116

Introduction

Steck-Vaughn's *Vocabulary in Context* series offers parents and educators high-quality, curriculum-based products that align with the Common Core Standards for English Language Arts for grades 2–9.

Each unit in the *Vocabulary in Context* books includes:

- fiction and/or nonfiction selections, covering a wide variety of topics

- context activities, ascertaining that students understand what they have read

- vocabulary activities, challenging students to show their understanding of key vocabulary

- questions in a standardized-test format, helping prepare students for standardized exams

- word skills activities, targeting additional vocabulary words and vocabulary skills

- writing activities, providing assignments that encourage students to use the vocabulary words

Reading selection

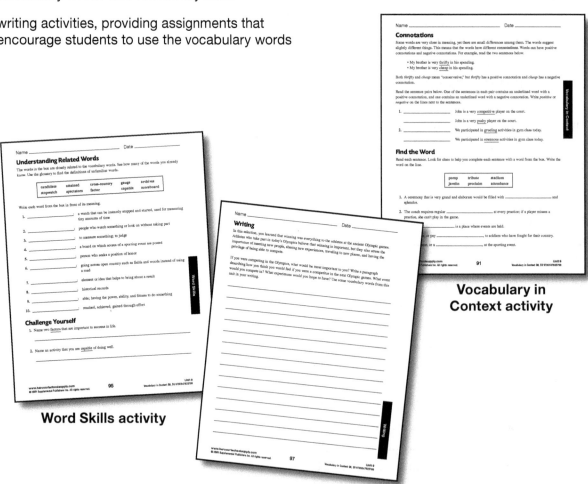

Word Skills activity

Writing activity

Vocabulary in Context activity

Determining Meaning Through Word Analysis

Words are made up of various combinations of the following parts: prefix, suffix, base word, and root. Analysis of these parts is another way to determine an unfamiliar word's meaning.

Prefix	a word part that is added to the beginning of another word or word part
Suffix	a word part that is added to the end of another word or word part
Base Word	a complete word to which a prefix and/or a suffix may be added
Root	a word part to which a prefix and/or a suffix must be added. A root cannot stand alone.

Prefixes

Prefix	Meaning	Example
a-, ab-	up, out; not; away	arise; abnormal; absent
anti-	against; prevents, cures	antiaircraft; antidote
contra-	opposed	contradict
de-	away from, off; down; reverse action of	derail; decline; defrost
dis-	lack of; not; away	distrust; dishonest; disarm
equi-	equal	equidistant
il-, im-, in-, ir-	not; in, into	illegal; investigate
inter-	between, among	international
mal-	bad	maltreat, malignant
mis-	wrong	misspell
non-	not	nonworking
post-	after in time or space	postpone
pre-	before	predawn
pro-	in favor of; forward, ahead	profamily; propel
re-	again; back	rethink; repay
semi-	half; twice in a period; partly	semicircle; semiannual; semiconscious
sub-	under, below	subzero
trans-	across; beyond	transcontinental; transcend
un-	not; reverse of	unhappy; unfasten

Suffixes

Noun Suffixes

Suffix	Example	Suffix	Example
-ance, -ancy, -ence	vigilance, vacancy, independence	*-ism*	realism, federalism
-ant	commandant, occupant	*-ist*	geologist
-ation, -ion, -ition	imagination, inspection, recognition	*-ity, -ty*	sincerity, frailty
-cy	accuracy	*-ment*	encouragement, commitment
-eer, -er	auctioneer, manager	*-ness*	kindness, fondness
-hood	womanhood, brotherhood	*-or*	counselor
-ice	cowardice, prejudice	*-ship*	ownership, worship
-ician	beautician, statistician	*-tude*	gratitude, solitude

Adjective Suffixes

Suffix	Meaning	Example
-able, -ible	able to be	readable, convertible
-al, -ant, -ar	relating to	musical, triumphant, polar
-ate	having, full of	passionate
-ful	full of	harmful
-ic, -ish	pertaining to, like	heroic, foolish
-ive	pertaining to	descriptive
-less	without	senseless
-like, -ly	like	lifelike, scholarly
-most	at the extreme	topmost
-ous	full of	furious
-or	one who	actor
-y	state of	funny

Verb Suffixes

Suffix	Meaning	Example
-ate, -fy	to make	activate, simplify
-en, -ise, -ize	to become	strengthen, merchandise, computerize

Adverb Suffixes

Suffix	Meaning	Example
-ily, -ly	manner	happily, quickly
-ward	toward	skyward
-wise	like	clockwise

Roots and Word Families

A word root cannot stand alone but must be combined with other word parts. A great many roots used in our language come from Greek or Latin. A single root can generate many English words.

Useful Greek Roots

Root	Meaning	Example
aster, astr	star	asterisk
auto	self, alone	autobiography
bibl, biblio	book	bibliography
bi, bio	life	biology
chron	time	chronology
cracy, crat	rule, government	democracy
gram, graph	write, draw, describe	grammar, paragraph
meter, metr	measure	barometer
neo	new	neoclassical
ortho	straight, correct	orthodontist, orthodox
phob	fear	claustrophobia
phon	sound	phonograph
psych	mind, soul, spirit	psychology
scope	see	telescope
tele	far, distant	television
therm	heat	thermometer

Useful Latin Roots

Root	Meaning	Example
capt, cept	take, have	capture, accept
cede, ceed, cess	go, yield, give way	secede, proceed, recess
dic, dict	speak, say, tell	dictate, dictionary
duc, duct	lead	introduce, conductor
fact, fect	do, make	factory, defect
ject	throw, hurl	eject, inject
mob, mot, mov	move	mobility, motion, movie
pon, pos, posit	place, put	opponent, deposit
port	carry	porter, portable
puls	throb, urge	pulsate, compulsory
scrib, script	write	prescribe, scripture
tain, ten, tent	hold	contain, tenant, attention
ven, vent	come	convention, event
vers, vert	turn	versatile, invert
vid, vis	see	video, vista
voc, vok	voice, call	vocal, invoke

A Vanishing Breed

by Howard Peet

Read the story. Think about the meanings of the **boldfaced** words. Then go back to the story. Underline the words or sentences that give you a clue to the meaning of each **boldfaced** word.

Commander Barry and Captain Sara were roasting marshmallows over a fire on the beach. Suddenly Sara's wrist telephone beeped. General Johnson's voice shouted, "There has been a **mishap** on Jupiter. Your **mission** is to fly there immediately and bring back the remaining members of the team stationed there."

In the **twilight**, the flames from the fire seemed to push back the darkness. "I hate to leave, but I **realize** how much those people need us," Barry said.

They put out the fire, turned on their rocket backpacks and flew to the Houston launching pad. Their spaceship, the *Pegasus*, stood ready for takeoff. Barry and Sara scrambled aboard, and the ship blasted off.

Barry checked the instrument panel. The speedometer showed a speed of 20,000 miles per hour. Barry called the command center for an **estimate** of the time needed to fly to Jupiter. A reply came back at once: "Over two years at your pace. You have almost 400 million miles to go. You must increase to warp speed so you can arrive sooner."

A few days later, Sara and Barry reached the **vicinity** of Jupiter. They marveled at the twelve moons orbiting the huge planet. Slowly the *Pegasus* settled onto Jupiter's surface. Near the landing site an American flag was waving over a group of silver tents.

Randy, the leader of the Jupiter team, greeted Sara and Barry. He explained that the party had been on Jupiter for a whole year. One day, completely by surprise, their group was attacked by space pirates. Randy's crew was at a **disadvantage** because the **invaders'** laser rays were so much more **effective** than their own weapons. The enemy's laser-ray **assault** injured Randy's son and **demolished** the party's spaceship. At the **completion** of the attack, Randy and his party were left stranded on the huge planet.

Sara and Barry took Randy and his crew aboard the *Pegasus*. The spaceship roared away from Jupiter. Randy was nervously watching the large screen in the ship's control room when he saw something. "Here comes the enemy spaceship. I know it is the same ship by its name—*Rats*—printed on the side."

Sara tried to steer away from *Rats*, but the two spaceships **collided**. During the confusion following the crash, four strange creatures from the *Rats* ship entered the *Pegasus*. Each creature had a name printed on its spacesuit. The names were Pam, Tolip, Oidar, and Lareneg.

Lareneg called out an order to his followers: "Tie these people up and lock them in a cell on *Rats*."

Barry calmly pointed his finger at the four creatures and shouted, "Star!" With that, all four creatures vanished and so did the spaceship *Rats*.

Sara checked out the damage to the ship and reported that the damage was not very **severe**. "However, it's going to be a long, slow trip home," she said.

Randy looked at Barry and asked, "How did you know what to do?"

Barry grinned. "Do you remember hearing about a tribe of creatures who broke away from the Kingdom of Neptune to become space pirates? They settled near here back in the year 2000. They named themselves after their leader, Enog. Enog was powerful, but he had one weakness—his name. If someone said it backwards, he would vanish."

"When I saw those names on the spacesuits, I realized the names could be read backwards. 'Pam' is 'map,' and she was the **navigator**. 'Oidar' is 'radio,' and he was the radio operator. The other names were spelled backwards also. It crossed my mind that if I said the name of their spaceship backwards, they might all vanish, just like Enog did."

Mercury Venus Earth Mars Jupiter Saturn Uranus Neptune

Context Clues

For each sentence write the letter of the word or phrase that is closest in meaning to the word or words in italics. Use context clues to help you choose the correct answer.

_____ **1.** After he punched Officer Santos, Dan was jailed for *assault*.

    A robbery   **B** rudeness   **C** vandalism   **D** violent attack

_____ **2.** A car crossed the center line of the highway and *collided* with another car, causing great damage.

    A narrowly missed   **B** crashed into   **C** scratched   **D** raced

_____ **3.** The deadline for the *completion* of the building was only one month away, but many workers believed it would take at least six more months to finish it.

    A starting   **B** finishing   **C** painting   **D** destruction

_____ **4.** Hurricane Molly *demolished* the coast, leaving houses, stores, and factories in ruins.

    A rained on   **B** chilled   **C** destroyed   **D** missed

_____ **5.** One *disadvantage* of living on an island is the difficulty of getting to the mainland and back in stormy weather.

    A pleasure   **B** handicap   **C** accident   **D** convenience

_____ **6.** Some doctors believe aspirin may be an *effective* treatment for heart disease because it thins the blood so that the blood can flow better.

    A useful   **B** deadly   **C** enjoyable   **D** false

_____ **7.** When an airline gives the arrival time of a flight, it is the airline's best *estimate* of how long the trip should take.

    A hope   **B** calculation   **C** rule   **D** decision

_____ **8.** The people on the west coast of Europe feared the Viking *invaders*, who easily overpowered the defenders of the coastal towns.

    A traders   **B** spies   **C** poets   **D** attackers

Name _____ Date _____

_____ **9.** Some people think that the Great Chicago Fire started with a *mishap* in Mrs. O'Leary's barn. O'Leary's cow kicked over a lantern, setting fire to the barn. The fire spread through much of the city.

      A benefit   **B** accident   **C** adventure   **D** demonstration

_____ **10.** Sergeant Amaya's dangerous *mission* was to rescue miners trapped a mile underground.

      A flight   **B** prank   **C** party   **D** task

_____ **11.** To go through a narrow, rocky channel in foggy weather, a ship needs a good *navigator*.

      A cabin boy   **C** helper on the shore

      B recreation director   **D** person who plots the course

_____ **12.** You will *realize* the importance of a college education when you begin looking for a job.

      A argue against   **B** be discouraged by   **C** forget   **D** understand

_____ **13.** In seventeenth-century New England, laws were very *severe*. For example, children who disobeyed their parents could be publicly whipped.

      A harsh   **B** wise   **C** foolish   **D** fair

_____ **14.** Since the cyclists did not have lights on their bicycles, they stopped riding at *twilight*.

      A noon   **B** midmorning   **C** sunset   **D** midnight

_____ **15.** When we drove downtown, we stayed away from the *vicinity* of the stadium to avoid the heavy pregame traffic.

      A violence   **B** neighborhood   **C** distant area   **D** noise

Name _____ Date _____

Word Maze

All the words in the box are hidden in the maze. The words can be arranged forward, backward, up, down, and diagonally. Circle each word as you find it and cross the word off the list. Different words may overlap and use the same letter.

assault	collide	completion	demolish	disadvantage
effective	estimate	invaders	mishap	mission
navigator	realize	severe	twilight	vicinity

E S T I M A T E G B N D B

V F A K R J D M J S A I F

I L F X W M S I R E V S I

C S D E Q U T S E V I A N

I O E X C U A H A E G D V

N Y M F O T T A L R A V A

I A O P L W I P I E T A D

T S L Z L Y O V Z C O N E

Y S I N I E N C E H R T R

F A S V D L T P S X V A S

M U H A E O B I D Q U G K

T L U M I S S I O N P E N

E T W I L I G H T N D H C

Standardized Test Practice

Circle the letter of the word that is most nearly *opposite* in meaning to the capitalized word.

TIP

Always read all the answer choices. Many choices may make sense. Only one answer choice has the opposite meaning as the capitalized word.

1. EFFECTIVE

   A evil   **B** costly   **C** useless   **D** attractive

2. COLLIDE

   A sell   **B** clash   **C** jolt   **D** separate

3. COMPLETION

   A ending   **B** result   **C** middle   **D** beginning

4. SEVERE

   A harsh   **B** mild   **C** cheerful   **D** dull

5. DEMOLISH

   A destroy   **B** solve   **C** build   **D** explore

Circle the letter of the word that is closest in meaning to the capitalized word.

6. ASSAULT

   A persuade   **B** greet   **C** command   **D** attack

7. MISHAP

   A sense   **B** accident   **C** detail   **D** story

8. INVADER

   A defender   **B** explorer   **C** voter   **D** attacker

9. DISADVANTAGE

   A benefit   **B** weakness   **C** value   **D** disguise

10. MISSION

    A tool   **B** location   **C** concern   **D** task

      Vocabulary in Context, G6 SV 9780547625799

Multiple-Meaning Words

Many words have more than one meaning. For example, look at the word *star* in the following sentences.

My cousin Jesse is a basketball *star* at her school.

People gazed at the bright *star* in the clear sky.

In the first sentence, *star* refers to a person who is outstanding. In the second sentence, *star* refers to a heavenly body shining in the night sky. Each of the following pairs of sentences uses the same word. If this italicized word has the same meaning in both sentences, write *same*. If the word has a different meaning, write *different*.

_____ **1. A** Corporal Jones's *mission* was to rescue ten children caught in a severe storm.

B At the *mission* in St. Augustine, the priests have a long tradition of helping people.

_____ **2. A** Fortunately, the *navigator* of the smaller ship, Captain Chang, kept the two ships from colliding.

B Imagine the difficulties a *navigator* faced in sailing to North America in 1492!

_____ **3. A** Every evening at *twilight*, the bells at the mission ring.

B My grandparents have slowed down in their *twilight* years, but they still like to travel.

_____ **4. A** My brother never fully *realized* how much talent he had as a distance runner.

B The company *realized* a profit of ten million dollars last year.

_____ **5. A** Father studied the carpenter's *estimate* closely to see if all the costs were included.

B Our *estimate* of the new coach was that she was demanding, but likeable.

Understanding Related Words

The words in the box can be related to the vocabulary words. See how many of the words you already know. Use the glossary to find the definitions of unfamiliar words.

advantageous	collision	demolition	disband
disorderly	dissolve	effect	ineffective
invade	invasion	navigate	realization

Write the letter of the situation that best shows the meaning of the boldfaced word.

Example:

__B__ **hinder**

   A A crossing guard assists a child across a street.

   B A worker places a boulder in a roadway.

   C A fan watches a baseball game.

_____ **1. ineffective**

   A A player uses a pencil to hit a baseball.

   B A bus driver takes aspirin to cure a headache.

   C A student works hard to learn how to play a musical instrument.

_____ **2. navigate**

   A A bird sits on its nest.

   B An airline pilot plans the best course for a flight.

   C A ship's captain sleeps in his cabin.

_____ **3. invade**

   A A horse enters its stall.

   B Your best friend pays you a visit.

   C An army marches into an enemy country.

_____ **4. advantageous**

   A You set aside enough time to study for tests.

   B You tease a snarling dog.

   C You receive penalties in a hockey game.

_____ **5. demolition**

   A Workers tear down a building.

   B Architects draw plans for a house.

   C A train screeches to a halt.

Word Skills

Name _____   Date _____

The Latin Prefix *dis-*

The common prefix *dis-* can mean "apart" (*dismiss*), "opposite of" (*disbelief*), or "refuse to" (*disassociate*). Refer to these three meanings as you answer the items below.

1. The teacher scolded the class for being *disorderly*.

   Disorderly means _____.

2. Temperatures over one hundred degrees cause people *discomfort*.

   Discomfort means _____.

3. After many arguments, the club decided to *disband*, never to meet again.

   Disband means _____.

4. One warm, sunny winter day the snow *dissolved* into trickles of water.

   Dissolved means _____.

5. The two sisters wanted to get a pet boa constrictor, but the girls' parents *disapproved* of the idea.

   Disapproved means _____.

6. After my friend's brother gave us wrong information three times, we started to *distrust* him.

   Distrust means _____.

7. My dog *disappeared* into the woods, but after much searching we finally found him.

   Disappeared means _____.

8. I used to *dislike* the taste of pepper, but I've finally learned to enjoy its flavor.

   Dislike means _____.

Word Skills

Writing

Imagine that you have been sent on a rescue mission to another country. Write about your experience.
Answer these questions in your story:

• Who was involved in your mission?

• Where did you go on your mission?

• Who were you sent to rescue?

• What problems did you face during your mission?

• How did your mission turn out?

Be sure to use some of the vocabulary words from this unit in your story.

_____

_____

_____

_____

_____

_____

_____

_____

_____

_____

_____

Writing

Annie Dodge Wauneka

by James Coomber

Read the selection. Think about the meanings of the **boldfaced** words. Then go back to the selection.
Underline the words or sentences that give you a clue to the meaning of each **boldfaced** word.

It has been said that we are on Earth to serve others. That is exactly what Annie Dodge Wauneka, a Native American of Navajo descent, spent her life doing. This selection focuses on the way she met challenges on an Arizona reservation.

The Presidential Medal of Freedom, America's highest civilian honor, is an award of appreciation given to individuals who have made great **contributions** to **society**. In 1963, President Lyndon Johnson gave this award to an Arizona Navajo leader, Annie Dodge Wauneka.

When Annie was a teenager, her father, Chee Dodge, became head of the Navajo Tribal Council. Annie often attended Council meetings with her father. At these meetings she heard many important tribal **issues** discussed. Annie, a shy girl, observed what was going on, but she did not say anything. Her father, noticing her shyness, **assured** her that she could **express** her opinions. He told her that being young was no reason to avoid speaking up. Even teenagers had the right to **participate** in tribal meetings. And participate she did.

When she was in her twenties, Annie Dodge Wauneka was elected to the Navajo Tribal Council. For twenty-eight years she was chairperson of the Council's Health and Welfare Committee. She used this position to begin her fight against a longtime enemy of the Navajo—tuberculosis. This disease **claimed** many lives on the Navajo reservation every year.

Wauneka faced numerous obstacles in her **efforts** to fight this disease. Living **conditions** were a great problem. Impure drinking water helped spread the disease, and the dirt floors of many homes resulted in unsanitary conditions. In addition, Navajo medicine men often did not appreciate the benefits of modern medicine and **opposed** Annie's plans for treatment and prevention. Navajos who did become hospitalized often tried to escape.

Wauneka worked tirelessly to solve these problems. She told her people that unclean conditions such as dirt floors cause disease, and she helped them get money for new homes. She went on the radio and for ten years gave information on tuberculosis to the people in their native language. She instructed people that with a disease like tuberculosis, **prompt** attention and **immediate** treatment are often a matter of life and death. She spent many hours assuring patients that the hospital was for their **benefit**.

Wauneka's struggles brought **results**. The reservation water systems were improved, and people could rely on having pure water. The number of Navajos who got medical help **increased** greatly. Even the medicine men started to work with the doctors rather than against them. Gradually, the Navajos began to realize that better living conditions result in healthier people.

Thanks to Annie Dodge Wauneka, tuberculosis is no longer a serious health problem for the Navajos.

Name _____   Date _____

Context Clues

For each sentence write the letter of the word or phrase that is closest in meaning to the word or words in italics. Use context clues to help you choose the correct answer.

_____   **1.** Alicia was afraid to go on the roller coaster, but her brother *assured* her that the ride was perfectly safe. She went on and enjoyed the ride.

    A convinced   **B** lied to   **C** refused to tell   **D** expressed doubts to

_____   **2.** Several top rock bands gave a concert for the *benefit* of the survivors of the earthquake. The concert raised money for food, clothing, and shelter.

    A release   **B** help   **C** memorial   **D** majority

_____   **3.** The grateful parrot owner *claimed* his lost bird after the bird told the finders its name and address.

    A collected   **B** scolded   **C** never found   **D** chained

_____   **4.** The doctor was shocked to see people living in such terrible *conditions*. The building was crumbling, there was no indoor plumbing, and dirt was everywhere.

    A confusion   **B** conflicts   **C** situations   **D** moods

_____   **5.** Jonas Salk made a major *contribution* to the field of medicine when he developed a vaccine for polio that helped millions of people.

    A misjudgment of   **B** comment about   **C** criticism of   **D** addition to

_____   **6.** With a great deal of *effort*, we finally scaled the 14,692-foot-high Matterhorn in the Swiss Alps. We were exhausted when we reached the top.

    A work   **B** talk   **C** luck   **D** equipment

_____   **7.** After scoring the winning run, Ventura *expressed* his thanks to the cheering crowd by tipping his hat.

    A denied   **B** took back   **C** communicated   **D** faked

_____   **8.** Margaret Mead is famous for her study of Samoan *society*. She wrote extensively about the Samoans' social order and their way of life.

    A community   **B** war   **C** art   **D** equipment

_____ **9.** Cucumbers can grow huge; one cucumber *increased* in size until it was over ten feet long.

    A expanded   **B** quickly shrank   **C** rotated   **D** gradually lessened

_____ **10.** Should all bicycle riders be required to wear a helmet? This *issue* was debated in the town meeting.

    A topic   **B** tragedy   **C** confusion   **D** research

_____ **11.** The owl butterfly has few enemies to *oppose* it. It scares off attackers because its wing spots look like the eyes of a large owl.

    A defend   **B** pose for   **C** go against   **D** observe

_____ **12.** Will you *participate in* softball again, or will you sit out this season?

    A pass up   **B** observe   **C** quit   **D** take part in

_____ **13.** Because of the *prompt* medical attention the crash victims received, many of them survived.

    A severe   **B** tragic   **C** quick   **D** delayed

_____ **14.** As *a result* of her brave deeds, Captain Rivera received the Medal of Honor.

    A a cause   **B** a condition   **C** an outcome   **D** an event

_____ **15.** When lightning hit our tree, the flash of light was accompanied by *an immediate* crack of thunder. It seemed as if the tree exploded.

    A an instant   **B** a distant   **C** a muffled   **D** a quiet

Vocabulary in Context

Word Maze

All the words in the list below are hidden in the maze. The words are arranged forward, backward, up, down, and diagonally. Circle each word as you find it and cross the word off the list. Different words may overlap and use the same letter.

assured	benefit	claimed	conditions	contribution
efforts	express	immediate	increase	issue
oppose	participate	prompt	results	society

```
C   O   N   D   I   T   I   O   N   S   A   P
L   O   P   P   O   S   E   I   I   J   R   A
A   B   N   R   D   H   Q   S   M   E   M   R
I   S   E   T   O   Z   U   S   M   F   E   T
M   T   Y   N   R   M   X   U   E   F   X   I
E   A   J   V   E   I   P   E   D   O   P   C
D   C   Q   M   U   F   B   T   I   R   R   I
P   L   T   K   A   W   I   U   A   T   E   P
R   E   S   U   L   T   S   T   T   S   S   A
G   I   N   C   R   E   A   S   E   I   S   T
C   L   A   S   S   U   R   E   D   K   O   E
S   O   C   I   E   T   Y   S   O   F   A   N
```

Standardized Test Practice

Circle the letter of the word that is closest in meaning to the capitalized word.

> **TIP**
> Always read all the answer choices. Many choices may make sense. Only one answer choice has the same or almost the same meaning as the capitalized word.

1. ASSURE

   A trouble   **B** alarm   **C** inform   **D** guarantee

2. BENEFIT

   A disadvantage   **B** harm   **C** aid   **D** temptation

3. CLAIM

   A take   **B** devour   **C** refuse   **D** dig

4. CONTRIBUTION

   A award   **B** donation   **C** claim   **D** completion

5. EFFORT

   A mishap   **B** laziness   **C** career   **D** labor

6. CONDITION

   A strength   **B** climate   **C** state   **D** contribution

7. IMMEDIATE

   A important   **B** instant   **C** late   **D** fortunate

8. INCREASE

   A complete   **B** enlarge   **C** reduce   **D** fold

9. PARTICIPATE

   A oppose   **B** observe   **C** decline   **D** share

10. RESULT

   A opportunity   **B** source   **C** mission   **D** effect

11. EXPRESS

   A say   **B** realize   **C** deny   **D** give

12. OPPOSED

   A disguised   **B** assured   **C** resisted   **D** welcomed

Vocabulary in Context

Understanding Related Words

The words in the box can be related to the vocabulary words. See how many of the words you already know. Use the glossary to find the definitions of unfamiliar words.

associate	assurance	beneficial	decrease	effortless
expression	opponent	participation	sociable	sociology

Write the word from the box that is most clearly related to the situation described in each sentence.

1. _____ Sports such as swimming and running have been found to be very helpful in maintaining good health.

2. _____ After only two months on his diet, Theo dropped from 205 pounds to 185.

3. _____ On Friday night we play our rivals in basketball, the Gonzales Middle School Gators.

4. _____ Maya loves to meet people, and she enjoys parties.

5. _____ Mr. Cho was in such good shape that his exercising seemed easy and painless.

6. _____ Fiona gave me her promise that she would not tell my secret to anyone.

7. _____ The saying "to pull the wool over someone's eyes" comes from the days when men wore wigs; a person might trick the wearer of a wig by pulling the wig over the wearer's eyes.

8. _____ Mrs. Chesniak's business partner at the Maple Street Candy Company was her longtime friend, Alice Randall.

9. _____ Professor Zamora was an expert in the study of the beliefs and values of various groups in society.

10. _____ Many students at Pierce Middle School go out for after-school sports or clubs.

Word Skills

Understanding Multiple-Meaning Words

The box in this exercise contains a boldfaced word with its definitions. Read the definitions and then the sentences that use the word. Write the letter of the definition that applies to each sentence.

> **issue**
>
> **a.** publication of a magazine or periodical (noun)
>
> **b.** to pass out, distribute (verb)
>
> **c.** a matter of disagreement; a question or point of discussion (noun)

_____ 1. Society members argued about the *issue* of increasing their taxes.

_____ 2. Coach Medford *issued* uniforms to each team member.

_____ 3. Mrs. Lee *issued* a dictionary to each student in her class.

_____ 4. The August *issue* of *National Geographic* featured an article about Greece.

_____ 5. The principal assured the students that they could discuss any *issues* that concerned them.

True or False

Decide whether each statement is true (**T**) or false (**F**) based on the meaning of the word in italics. Write *T* or *F* on each line. Use the glossary or a dictionary if you need help.

_____ 1. A person sitting alone on a desert island is an example of a *society*.

_____ 2. United States senators debate *issues* of national importance.

_____ 3. By answering a question thoughtfully, you *contribute* to a class discussion.

_____ 4. Regular exercise is *beneficial* to your health.

_____ 5. There is usually a lot of *participation* by airline passengers in navigating the flight path.

_____ 6. You cannot *claim* a lost item when it is in the Lost and Found Department.

_____ 7. There was an *expression* of happiness on her face when she realized that she had lost her favorite backpack.

_____ 8. Volunteers reminded people to vote in an effort to *decrease* the number of voters.

_____ 9. Teachers appreciate students who are *prompt*.

_____ 10. In the Revolutionary War, the British army and the American colonial army were *opponents*.

Word Skills

The Latin Roots *socius* and *bene*

Socius is a Latin word meaning "companion" or "sharing." Several words contain the *socius* root and deal in some way with people or companions. Match each definition on the right with the appropriate word on the left. Write the letter of the correct definition on the line.

_____ **1.** associate (noun)   **a.** acting in a friendly manner (adj.)

_____ **2.** society   **b.** a group of people with the same customs and beliefs (noun)

_____ **3.** sociable   **c.** the study of people in groups (noun)

_____ **4.** socialize   **d.** to take part in activities (verb)

_____ **5.** sociology   **e.** a friend or partner (noun)

The word *benefit* and the related word *beneficial* come from the Latin root *bene*, meaning "well." The following words also contain the root *bene*: *benefactor, beneficiary, beneficent*. Match each definition on the right with the appropriate word on the left. Write the letter of the correct definition on the line.

_____ **6.** benefit (noun)   **a.** a person who receives help (noun)

_____ **7.** beneficial   **b.** showing kindness or doing good for others (adj.)

_____ **8.** beneficent   **c.** a person who gives help (noun)

_____ **9.** benefactor   **d.** a performance that raises money for a cause (noun)

_____ **10.** beneficiary   **e.** producing helpful effects (adj.)

Dictionary Skills

Write the words in alphabetical order, one word on each line. Then turn to the glossary and find each word. Write its meaning on the line.

opponent	effortless	sociology	expression	sociable

1. _____

2. _____

3. _____

4. _____

5. _____

Word Skills

Name _____   Date _____

Writing

What do you think is the most important scientific contribution of this century? Why do you think society has benefitted from this innovation? Be sure to use some of the vocabulary words from this unit in your response.

_____

_____

_____

_____

_____

_____

_____

_____

_____

_____

_____

_____

Vocabulary in Context G6, SV 9780547625799

Writing

How the Sun Came

by James Coomber

Read the story. Think about the meanings of the **boldfaced** words. Then go back to the story. Underline the words or sentences that give you a clue to the meaning of each **boldfaced** word.

Myths are old, traditional stories that imaginatively explain why the world is the way it is. The following myth has been told by the Cherokee Indians to explain how sunlight came to their land.

Long ago, darkness draped itself across the land, covering everything with its dark fingers. Animals kept bumping into one another and complaining, "It is so dark. What we need is light." Finally the animals called a **conference** to explore the problem **jointly**.

The redheaded woodpecker began, "They say some people on the other side of Earth **possess** light. Maybe one of us could go there and bring back some light. Who shall go?"

The opossum spoke up. "I can hide a piece of the sun in my bushy, furry tail. I will go." As the opossum traveled to the east, the sky became brighter and brighter until it was as **brilliant** as a sparkling diamond. The opossum had to squint to keep from being blinded by this brilliant light. To this day the opossum's eyes are tiny from this squinting, and opossums **prefer** darkness to daylight.

The opossum arrived at his **destination**, the sun. He snatched a small **segment** of the sun, and he put it in the fur of his tail. But the sun was a burning fireball, with heat so intense that it scorched his fur. When he returned, his tail **lacked** fur (that is why opossums' tails are bare today), and he had no light.

Next the buzzard volunteered to make the trip. In his **opinion** a tail was no place to hold the sun. "I am too smart to put the sun on my tail," he said. "I'll set it on my head." So the buzzard journeyed eastward until he came to the sun. From high in the sky he **plunged**, grabbed a piece of the sun, and set it on his head. But the hot sun burned off his head feathers, which explains how the buzzard came to be bald. He, too, had failed to bring back the light.

The creatures now were very **discouraged**. They were tired of the darkness that wrapped its cold arms around them. The need for light seemed more **urgent**. Everyone agreed that the opossum and the buzzard had done their best. They wondered what else they could do to get the light.

A small, soft voice spoke up. "This is Grandmother Spider speaking," said she. "**I suspect** it is up to me to bring you light. At least, I would really like to try." The others agreed to let her make the attempt.

Before she headed eastward, Grandmother Spider made a bowl of wet clay. With her bowl she approached the sun, spinning a thread behind her so she could find her way home. As quiet as she was, neither the sun nor the sun people noticed Grandmother Spider. Gently, she took only a tiny piece of the sun and put it in her bowl. Then westward she made her way, following the thread she had spun before. The sun's light spread like a flowing river before her as she went. You can observe today that a spider's web has a sun-shape in the middle with rays spreading out from it.

Everyone was **indebted** to Grandmother Spider and promised to remember her always. The world was **transformed** by the light.

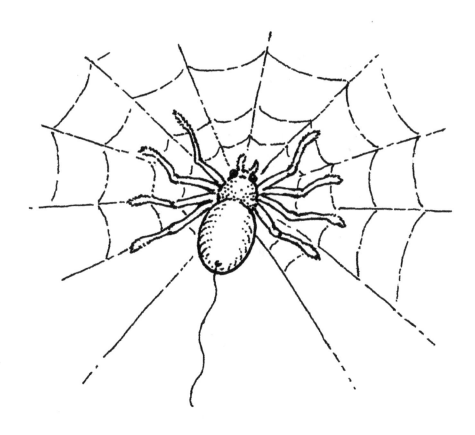

Name _____ Date _____

Understanding Figurative Language

Writers often use figurative language, or figures of speech, to help their readers visualize or imagine the images they are describing. Below are three types of figurative language that appear in the myth "How the Sun Came." Read about these figures of speech. Then answer the questions that follow.

Simile: A simile compares two things using the words *like* or *as*.

Examples: The water was as cold as ice.

His legs felt like lead as he trudged to the office.

Metaphor: A metaphor compares two things by stating that one thing *is* something else.

Examples: Her smile was the sun lighting up his world.

Life is a roller coaster, filled with ups and downs.

Personification: Personification gives an object human attributes or characteristics.

Examples: The sun smiled down on the children as they played.

The stars danced across the sky in a joyous dance.

Circle the letter of the sentence that correctly answers the question.

1. Which of the sentences from the story contains an example of **personification**?

   A Long ago, darkness draped itself across the land, covering everything with its dark fingers.

   B The need for light seemed more urgent.

   C You can observe today that a spider's web has a sun-shape in the middle with rays spreading from it.

2. Which of the sentences from the story contains an example of a **simile**?

   A Maybe one of us could go there and bring back some light.

   B The opossum arrived at his destination, the sun.

   C The sun's light spread like a flowing river before her as she went.

3. Which of the sentences from the story contains an example of a **metaphor**?

   A He snatched a small segment of the sun, and he put it in the fur of his tail.

   B But the sun was a burning fireball, with heat so intense that it scorched his fur.

   C So the buzzard journeyed eastward until he came to the sun.

4. Which of the sentences from the story contains an example of **personification**?

   A The opossum had to squint to keep from being blinded by this brilliant light.

   B He, too, had failed to bring back the light.

   C They were tired of the darkness that wrapped its cold arms around them.

Context Clues

For each sentence write the letter of the word or phrase that is closest in meaning to the word or words in italics. Use context clues to help you choose the correct answer.

_____ 1. The *most brilliant* star in the heavens is Sirius, the Dog Star; its radiant shine makes it easy to pick out at night.

    A densest   **C** nearest
    B most easily overlooked   **D** brightest

_____ 2. An annual dental convention is held in Chicago in February. It is the largest *conference* for dentists in the United States.

    A problem   **B** trip   **C** meeting   **D** society

_____ 3. When the temperature dropped to –72°F, the polar explorers had an *urgent* need for warmer clothing.

    A decreased   **B** serious   **C** little   **D** mild

_____ 4. Mrs. Hargrave was *discouraged*. She had failed her automobile driving test thirty-nine times.

    A poor   **B** downhearted   **C** cheerful   **D** nearsighted

_____ 5. Nineteen people in our town *are indebted* to Leroy Jones. These people have been rescued from drowning by Leroy during his job as a lifeguard.

    A owe money to   **B** owe thanks to   **C** are familiar with   **D** are related to

_____ 6. The first climb to the top of Mt. Everest was accomplished not by a single person but *jointly* by two people. One was Edmund Hillary of New Zealand, and the other was Tenzing Norgay of Nepal.

    A in one day   **B** fortunately   **C** together   **D** separately

_____ 7. In much of the Arctic during the winter, the sun never appears in the sky. This *lack* of sunshine is difficult for newcomers to get used to.

    A amount   **B** increase   **C** absence   **D** memory

_____ 8. I believe that wearing a bike helmet increases safety. It is my *opinion* that our town's law requiring people to wear a helmet while bicycling is a good one.

    A information   **B** judgment   **C** plan   **D** doubt

_____ **9.** Without a parachute, Lieutenant Chisov fell out of a plane at an altitude of nearly twenty-two thousand feet. Incredibly, he landed in a snow-filled ditch and survived his *plunge*.

    A task   **B** fall   **C** climb   **D** attempt

_____ **10.** To become an Olympic gymnast, one must *possess* the following qualities: strength, balance, a willingness to work hard, and a desire for perfection.

    A have   **B** observe   **C** appreciate   **D** lack

_____ **11.** My brother and I both love turkey. I *prefer* dark meat, but my brother favors light meat.

    A choose   **B** avoid   **C** plan for   **D** deserve

_____ **12.** The surgeon removed a small *segment* of the patient's intestine.

    A factor   **B** part   **C** whole   **D** result

_____ **13.** Before I finished the novel, I *suspected* that the hero would not catch the criminal. When I read the final chapter, I found that I was right—the villain got away.

    A discovered   **B** knew   **C** doubted   **D** guessed

_____ **14.** Water was piped in to irrigate the desert, and soon the desert was *transformed into* green farmland.

    A destroying   **B** changed into   **C** a result of the   **D** moved to

_____ **15.** Diego boarded a plane in Chicago. The plane's *destination* was San Francisco. Diego was going there to visit his brother.

    A name   **B** place of arrival   **C** place of departure   **D** navigator

Name _____   Date _____

Crossword Puzzle

Read the clues and write the correct answers in the squares. There are several vocabulary words in this puzzle.

Across

1. A place at the end of a trip
8. 2,000 pounds
9. String tied together making a device to catch fish
10. Abbr. street
12. Abbr. Parent Teachers Association
14. Abbr. compact disc
15. A meeting
20. Beliefs
21. To perform an action
22. Abbr. United States of America
24. That girl
25. A rowboat's paddle
27. Abbr. American Medical Association
29. Immediately necessary
31. Football cheer
32. Fe, ___ ___, fo, fum
33. To think it likely
37. Stick out your tongue and say ___ ___.
39. A certain amount of space; region
40. A piece; section

Down

1. To cause to lose hope
2. Abbr. saint
3. In the direction of; toward
4. Not out
5. Changes
6. A single time

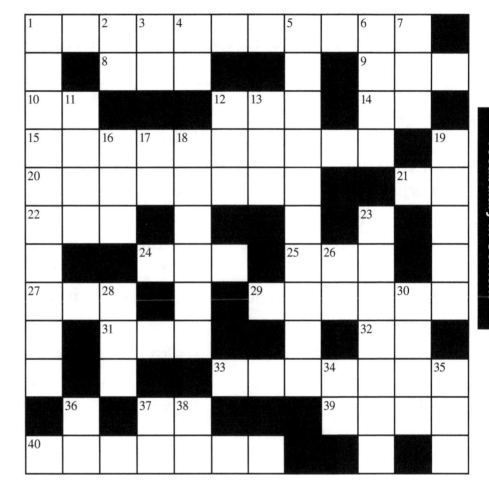

7. Man's name; rhymes with Ted
11. A cone-shaped toy, spun on its pointed end (plural)
12. Slang for a professional athlete
13. Comes after nine
16. ___ ___ ___ gara Falls
17. Abbr. footnote
18. Comes after seventh
19. Shared with someone else; done together
23. Likes best

26. Abbr. agriculture
28. Made by artists
30. Pleasing; well-behaved
34. Father
35. A light knock
36. Objective case of "I"
37. Morning hours
38. That man

Standardized Test Practice

Circle the letter of the word that is most nearly opposite in meaning to the capitalized word.

TIP

Always read all the answer choices. Many choices may make sense. Only one answer choice has the opposite meaning as the capitalized word.

Vocabulary in Context

1. BRILLIANT
   A angry   B bright   C dull   D serious   E cowardly

2. DESTINATION
   A beginning   B solution   C goal   D position   E fortune

3. DISCOURAGE
   A neglect   B disapprove   C deceive   D depress   E urge

4. INDEBTED
   A honorable   B ungrateful   C appreciative D thankful   E effective

5. LACK
   A shortage   B surplus   C effect   D emptiness   E disadvantage

6. OPINION
   A belief   B difficulty   C effect   D freedom   E fact

7. POSSESS
   A dispose   B make   C have   D keep   E assure

8. PREFER
   A choose   B dislike   C return   D realize   E elect

9. SEGMENT
   A part   B factor   C whole   D issue   E section

10. URGENT
    A serious   B effective   C strong   D important   E unnecessary

Synonyms and Antonyms

Remember that **synonyms** are words that have the same or almost the same meaning. **Antonyms** are words that have opposite meanings.

Decide if the following pairs of words are synonyms or antonyms. Write *S* for Synonym or *A* for Antonym.

_____ **1.** confer—discuss

_____ **2.** brilliance—dullness

_____ **3.** destiny—fate

_____ **4.** discouragement—hopefulness

_____ **5.** dispossess—take away

_____ **6.** encourage—criticize

_____ **7.** preference—dislike

_____ **8.** suspicion—distrust

_____ **9.** transfer—keep

_____ **10.** transmit—deliver

Dictionary Skills

Find the word *preference* in a dictionary and answer the questions.

1. What are the guide words for the page?

_____

2. Does the word *preference* come before or after the word *preferable*?

_____

3. Is the word *preference* an adjective, noun, or verb?

_____

4. How many syllables are in the word *preference*?

_____

5. What is one meaning of the word *preference*?

_____

Understanding Multiple-Meaning Words

The box in this exercise contains a boldfaced word with its definitions. Read the definitions and then the sentences that use the word. Write the letter of the definition that applies to each sentence.

> **suspect**
> **a.** a person who is considered guilty (noun)
> **b.** to think it likely; guess (verb)
> **c.** to believe to be guilty of something (verb)

_____ **1.** Police *suspected* Dirty Dan of participating in the burglary.

_____ **2.** I *suspect* Jamail will be very tired after running the ten-mile obstacle course.

_____ **3.** Who would have *suspected* that Mr. Medrano would arrive early?

_____ **4.** For hours the police questioned the *suspect*.

_____ **5.** Mrs. Singh *suspected* that Amar was struggling with the assignment and needed help.

Word Meaning

Write the letter of the situation that best shows the meaning of the boldfaced word.

_____ **1. transformation**

    A A boy had a pet rabbit named Scruffy.

    B People were walking to the train in the morning.

    C The caterpillar changed into a beautiful butterfly.

_____ **2. confer**

    A A teacher and a student met to talk about the student's work.

    B Two new restaurants have opened recently in our neighborhood.

    C We took several great photos at the zoo.

_____ **3. debt**

    A Nicholas finally put his money in the bank.

    B A classmate borrowed money from you.

    C Through hard work, Jessica became a fine athlete.

_____ **4. brilliance**

    A The carpenter studied the chair that he had built.

    B The students had no answer for the teacher's strange question.

    C The lake surface reflected the rays of the sun.

Word Skills

Writing

Grandmother Spider solved her community's problem of darkness by gathering a piece of the sun and bringing light to her friends. Imagine that you are a member of a community that is faced with a challenge or a problem. Write a story about how you could solve your community's problem. Use some of the vocabulary words from this unit in your story.

_____

_____

_____

_____

_____

_____

_____

_____

_____

_____

_____

Writing

The Black Hole

by Howard Peet

Read the story. Think about the meanings of the **boldfaced** words. Then go back to the story. Underline the words or sentences that give you a clue to the meaning of each **boldfaced** word.

The crew of the spaceship Silver Chariot think all is going well on their trip through outer space. Then they are mysteriously shaken and feel themselves being pulled toward a black hole!

The giant spaceship *Silver Chariot* sped silently toward the star Capella, forty-five light years from Earth and the most brilliant star in the Auriga constellation. The navigator, Tamika Bartlet, glanced at her computer screen. Right on course, she thought. She was pleased with the new computer. It had been **developed** to help her spacecraft **explore** deep space. The computer constantly **calculated** the ship's exact position, speed, and route. The computer was especially useful on this trip to explore the Auriga star system because no ship had ever been this far from Earth before. The voyage of the *Silver Chariot* had already done much to **expand** scientists' knowledge of distant star systems.

Suddenly, the entire crew was thrown to the left side of the ship. There was a sharp, unexpected increase in speed. An **exceptional** force from somewhere pulled the *Silver Chariot* off course. Alex Burness, the engineer, promptly turned the booster rocket to full blast. This **extreme** measure **produced** no effect. A tremendous pull of **gravity** sucked the ship closer to Capella. Then, in an instant, the brilliance of Capella was gone.

The voice of Captain Torrance came over the ship's loudspeaker. "Secure your seat belts. It seems that Capella, **classified** as a type K5 star, has just become a black hole, and we are being pulled toward it. A black hole occurs when a dying star begins cooling at its **core**. As the core cools, the star **collapses** and **creates** a great suction, something like a whirlpool. Anything near the collapsing star **contracts** and is pulled into the powerful whirlpool. Everything—from spaceship to planets—disappears into the core of the collapsing star—gone forever. That's the theory anyway. Our only hope is to keep cool heads, **concentrate** on doing our jobs, and try to increase our speed until we reach the speed of light. At that point, we may be able to escape the pull and get away from the black hole. Brace yourselves."

The *Silver Chariot* shook and trembled. There was an ear-shattering roar. The whirling force was showing no **mercy**. Then, incredibly, the ship was again soaring through space, past familiar stars. With the force of a slingshot, it had been flung back from where it came.

The ship sped faster than the speed of light toward what appeared to be Earth—an Earth, however, that seemed many times larger than it should have been. The *Silver Chariot* hurtled uncontrollably to the planet's surface. There was a series of crashes, a breaking of glass, a tumbling over what seemed like bushes, and finally, a thud.

The crew regained their senses and stared out the ship's portals into a vast powder-blue field. The ship's computer soon had the "field" identified—dense rows of giant strands of woven wool. In the distance, at the far edges of this landscape, huge chairs and tables sat like mountains. The computer supplied more information, the ship's present location: a carpeted room in a home near San Diego, California. With horror, Captain Torrance now realized the effect of the black hole's force on the spaceship. Ship and crew had been shrunk to the size of a deck of cards.

Several minutes later, the entire crew heard a giant call, "Johnny, time for your bath. Get your bath toys."

Among the toys that the Earth child grabbed was a tiny metal spaceship.

Name _____ Date _____

Context Clues

For each sentence write the letter of the word or phrase that is closest in meaning to the word or words in italics. Use context clues to help you choose the correct answer.

_____ 1. Luisa could not *calculate* the cost of the art supplies in her head. She needed paper and pencil to add so many numbers.

    A increase   **B** remember   **C** profit from   **D** figure

_____ 2. Canoeists *classify* rivers by how difficult or dangerous the rivers are. A Class I river is easy; a Class VI river is extremely dangerous.

    A grade   **B** prefer   **C** assault   **D** learn

_____ 3. The park ranger worried that the old silver mine might *collapse*, injuring visitors.

    A increase   **B** open   **C** fall in   **D** vary

_____ 4. "*Concentrate on* your race," my coach said. "Don't worry about the crowd or how cold it is."

    A Focus your attention on   **C** Struggle with
    B Pay no attention to   **D** Argue about

_____ 5. Because of the cold weather, the air inside my bike tires had *contracted*. The tires were almost flat.

    A become compressed   **C** increased
    B frozen   **D** exploded

_____ 6. Scientists believe that Earth's *core* is very hot. They've drilled deep into Earth, and the temperature increased as they drilled deeper.

    A climate   **B** destination   **C** outer surface   **D** center

_____ 7. Tornadoes sometimes form during powerful thunderstorms. The tornadoes are often more dangerous than the storms that *create* them.

    A dispose of   **B** cause   **C** invite   **D** destroy

_____ 8. The coach was given credit for *developing* an average basketball team into a state powerhouse.

    A forcing   **B** building   **C** talking   **D** destroying

_____ **9.** Sally Kristen Ride was *an exceptional* person. In 1983 she became the first American woman in space, aboard the space shuttle *Challenger*.

    A a fearful   **B** a courteous   **C** an unusual   **D** a cowardly

_____ **10.** More students attend our middle school each year. Classrooms are already crowded, but there is no money to *expand* the building.

    A close   **B** increase   **C** decrease   **D** decorate

_____ **11.** Roberto and Cameron set out on their bikes to *explore* the park. Neither had been to the park before, and they were curious about it.

    A assault   **B** neglect   **C** investigate   **D** hide in

_____ **12.** Some animals, like the penguin, can live in the *extreme* cold of Antarctica. As for me, I don't ever want to go where it's that cold.

    A calm   **B** severe   **C** slight   **D** gentle

_____ **13.** *Gravity* is weaker on the moon than it is on Earth. It would be a great place for basketball because you could jump really high.

    A Chemistry   **C** Sound
    B The speed of light   **D** The force that makes things fall

_____ **14.** The judge showed *mercy* on the young offender by lowering the fine.

    A cruelty to   **B** anger at   **C** distrust in   **D** willingness to forgive

_____ **15.** The hurricane *produced* huge waves that grew larger as the storm came nearer.

    A made   **B** classified   **C** collapsed   **D** invented

Vocabulary in Context

Vocabulary in Context G6, SV 9780547625799

Word Maze

All the words in the list below are hidden in the maze. The words are arranged forward, backward, up, down, and diagonally. Circle each word as you find it and cross the word off the list. Different words may overlap and use the same letter.

calculated	classification	collapses	concentrate	contract
core	creates	develop	exceptional	expand
explore	extreme	gravity	mercy	produce

C O L L A P S E S Q U F A G

O L E X C E P T I O N A L R

N M A G N E T A C V X G D A

C D C S U L P R O D U C E V

E K B O S X M A N O M R V I

N P E Y R I U L T W S E E T

T C M Q U E F V R N Q A L Y

R E E R E W Q I A F C T O T

A X R F X K X M C R H E P I

T P C V P P Y R T A J S H O

E L Y C A L C U L A T E D N

J O A K N J Z A V E O I H A

A R L A D P E F G O R S O L

C E I N Z E X T R E M E B N

42

Name _____ Date _____

Standardized Test Practice

Circle the letter of the word that is closest in meaning to the capitalized word.

TIP — Always read all the answer choices. Many choices may make sense. Only one answer choice has the same or almost the same meaning as the capitalized word.

1. CORE
   A conference   **B** outside   **C** reason   **D** center

2. CREATE
   A make   **B** undo   **C** transfer   **D** package

3. PRODUCE
   A manufacture   **B** restore   **C** dispose   **D** separate

4. MERCY
   A anger   **B** messiness   **C** knowledge   **D** kindness

5. DEVELOP
   A destroy   **B** commit   **C** grow   **D** express

Determine the relationship between the pair of capitalized words. Then decide which other word pair expresses a similar relationship. Circle the letter of this word pair.

6. EXPLORE: EXPLORATION
   A concentrate: concentration   **C** teach: teacher
   B pull: trigger   **D** bake: kitchen

7. GRAVITY: WEIGHT
   A fire: heat   **C** luxury: necessity
   B path: trail   **D** salt: pepper

8. COLLAPSE: EXPAND
   A understand: know   **C** forget: remember
   B shout: yell   **D** make: assemble

9. EXCEPTIONAL: UNUSUAL
   A gentle: tender   **C** broken: restored
   B harmless: hurtful   **D** bad: good

10. PRODUCE: DESTROY
    A trick: fool   **C** start: begin
    B hit: miss   **D** whittle: carve

Vocabulary in Context G6, SV 9780547625799

Understanding Multiple-Meaning Words

Each box in this exercise contains a boldfaced word with its definitions. Read the definitions and then the sentences that use the word. Write the letter of the definition that applies to each sentence.

> **contract**
> **a.** an agreement (noun)
> **b.** to draw together; to become smaller; to shrink (verb)
> **c.** to get or acquire (verb)

_____ **1.** According to the sales *contract*, the house will belong to Rachel after January 1.

_____ **2.** Looking in the microscope, Suki watched the organisms move toward one spot. In a matter of seconds, they would *contract* into a single mass.

_____ **3.** Under the workers' new *contract* with the owners, Saturdays and Sundays will always be considered nonworking days.

_____ **4.** When objects cool, they *contract*; as they become warmer, they expand.

_____ **5.** Since Jeremy started having a flu shot at the start of each winter, he has never *contracted* the flu.

> **concentrate**
> **a.** to bring together in one place (verb)
> **b.** to give careful attention to (verb)
> **c.** a substance that is especially strong, not weakened (noun)

_____ **6.** Jeff *concentrated* on reading the directions before he started assembling the model airplane.

_____ **7.** Officer Vorucci *concentrated* her police patrols in the area of the criminals' hide-out.

_____ **8.** Most of the population of Canada is *concentrated* within several hundred miles of the Canadian-United States border.

_____ **9.** The orange juice was a *concentrate*, so Luis added water to it before drinking it.

_____ **10.** It was so noisy in the lunchroom that Chan could not *concentrate* on his book.

Understanding Related Words

The words in the box can be related to the vocabulary words. See how many of the words you already know. Use the glossary to find the definitions of unfamiliar words.

classic	concentration	decrease	design	exception
exit	exploration	exterior	extinguish	progress

Write the word from the box that best completes the meaning of the sentence.

_____ **1.** "If we do not _____ spending immediately," the mayor said, "this city will be broke within a week."

_____ **2.** The United States took a big leap forward in the _____ of space when Neil Armstrong took the first step on the moon.

_____ **3.** Rafael and Bill made rapid _____ down the river. The swift current helped move them along quickly in their canoe.

_____ **4.** The house's wooden _____ is in bad need of fresh paint. Many years of rain, snow, and sun have caused the old paint to crack and peel.

_____ **5.** Shakespeare's *King Lear* is a _____ play. It is one of the most famous plays ever written.

_____ **6.** People who leave early should use the _____ at the rear of the theater.

_____ **7.** Mark's _____ was broken by the loud noise from the back of the classroom, and he had a difficult time getting his thoughts back on his exam.

_____ **8.** Tickets cost $5.00 each for all regular-season baseball games. The only _____ is the last game, when tickets are half price.

_____ **9.** When you leave camp, _____ your campfire completely. If you don't, it could start up again and cause a forest fire.

_____ **10.** Sachi is trying to _____ a better treehouse. She thinks there is a way to make one big enough for at least five people.

Word Skills

The Latin Prefixes *ex-* and *pro-*

A common prefix, *ex-* usually means "out" or "out of." For example, the target word *explore* comes from a Latin word meaning "to search *out*." The related word *exit* means "to go *out*." Use a dictionary to learn the meaning of the other *ex-* words in the list below. Then write the word from the list that best completes the meaning of each sentence.

exaggerate	examine	excess	exploit	extraordinary

_____ **1.** Uncle Raymond tells many stories about his adventures. My favorite one is about his _____ in East Africa in which he helped capture ivory traders.

_____ **2.** Aiko wanted to _____ the old steam engine more closely to see how it worked.

_____ **3.** "Don't _____," Ben said. "Tell me what really happened."

_____ **4.** My brother is a magician on the basketball court. Some of his fakes and jumps are truly _____.

_____ **5.** The scoutmaster warned his troops about packing _____ gear. He said the scouts should take only things they really needed.

The prefix *pro-* is found in many English words. It comes from the Latin word meaning "forward." The target word *produce* comes from the Latin words *pro* and *ducere* ("to lead"). *Produce* literally means "to lead forward." The related word *progress* also includes the Latin word *pro*. *Progress* means "to go forward."

Match each of the following *pro* words with its definition. Write the word on the line next to the correct definition.

profound	prolong	propel	protest	provoke

_____ **6.** to make angry

_____ **7.** to push; to make go forward

_____ **8.** to cause to last longer

_____ **9.** to speak out against

_____ **10.** showing great thought; deeply felt

Writing

Imagine you are an astronaut exploring a distant planet. This strange world is filled with odd plants and animals. The gravity on the planet is only one-tenth of the gravity on Earth. Write a report to mission control describing your experiences and observations on this planet. Use some of the vocabulary words from this unit in your report.

_____

_____

_____

_____

_____

_____

_____

_____

_____

_____

_____

_____

_____

_____

Vocabulary in Context G6, SV 9780547625799

Writing

The Dogholes

by Howard Peet

Read the story. Think about the meanings of the **boldfaced** words. Then go back to the story. Underline the words or sentences that give you a clue to the meaning of each **boldfaced** word.

Along the rough and rocky coast of California in the mid-1800s, "doghole schooners" sailed in and out of inlets to collect logs for America's sawmills. In the following story, you will find out why these sturdy little ships were given their odd name.

In the evenings, after dinner, we could sometimes persuade the captain to sit by the fireplace and tell **yarns** about his days as a ship's officer on a **vessel** called the *Artful Dodger*. No matter what other delights or joys the day had held for us, this was always the **supreme** pleasure. With each movement of his arms throwing dark shadows on the walls and with his white beard glowing in the firelight, the captain could hold our attention for hours. Now and then, a **screech** from an owl somewhere outside in the deep darkness would make us jump.

We each had our own **individual** favorites among his tales, and each of us felt we had the **right** to hear the ones we liked best. The ones I wanted most to hear were those that told about the work the *Artful Dodger* was built to do. She was the type of ship known as a doghole schooner, which carried logs down the dangerous coast of California. She had a crew of four and one **officer**, the captain. The crews of these schooners were usually men from Scandinavia, which is why the **local** people called the dogholers the "Scandinavian Navy."

The job of a doghole schooner was to sail **parallel** to the coast and slip into and out of the narrow inlets known as dogholes. After entering the inlets, the crew would try to grab a load of logs and escape without being left high and dry by a falling tide or getting smashed by a sudden storm. The doghole inlets are no more than cuts in the cliffs. Most are so small that sailors claimed only a dog could turn around in one. A ship in such waters required a crew with a lot of experience. Other types of ships could take on and train several new sailors at once, but on board these doghole schooners there was little room for **amateurs**.

To load logs, the sailors used slides made of greased redwood. The slides had been built down the sides of the cliffs. Lumberjacks cut the trees in the coastal forests and prepared the logs for transport. The loading **technique** was remarkable. Huge logs were sent plunging down the slippery slides toward the tiny, bobbing doghole ship below. Timing was the trick. As the log whizzed down the slide, it had to be slowed just before reaching the schooner. To allow this, the last **section** of the slide, called the "clapper," was made so that it could be tipped upward. This had to be done at just exactly the right moment. If the clapperman's timing was off, the log would slam right through the schooner and **shatter** it. Such mishaps were not uncommon. Most doghole schooners went to the bottom after only three or four years at sea. On many **occasions** the *Artful Dodger* herself barely escaped destruction.

As soon as one story was finished, we would all **demand** another. Once the captain had turned his mind to the past and started with his stories, he was often willing to give in when we insisted on more. Many times the clock struck midnight before exhaustion turned our attention away from life aboard the *Dodger* and toward our beds.

Name _____ Date _____

Context Clues

For each sentence write the letter of the word or phrase that is closest in meaning to the word or words in italics. Use context clues to help you choose the correct answer.

Vocabulary in Context

_____ 1. Juan pitches regularly on his school's baseball team. He may just be *an amateur* now, but he dreams of making his living as a major-league player someday.

   A a hard worker   **B** a champion   **C** a nonprofessional   **D** a bad player

_____ 2. Kate didn't think it was fair that only Ben got to explain, so she *demanded* a chance to tell her side of the story.

   A strongly asked for   **B** quietly gave up   **C** laughed at   **D** ignored

_____ 3. Yoki was tired; Angel was bored; I was getting a headache. We all had our own *individual* reasons for leaving the party early.

   A made-up   **B** personal   **C** exciting   **D** secondhand

_____ 4. The people who live in the *local* area say The Crab Palace is the best restaurant here. Many visitors eat there, too, and speak highly of it.

   A crowded   **B** nearby   **C** remote   **D** dangerous

_____ 5. Jarrod hates to cook. There was only one *occasion*, as far as I can remember, when he made dinner.

   A dream   **B** future event   **C** time   **D** mistake

_____ 6. The *officers* on the ship will give orders and make sure the crew members obey them.

   A passengers   **B** equipment   **C** persons in charge   **D** guests

_____ 7. If we walk *parallel* to the fence, sooner or later we'll find the place where the horses have been getting out.

   A along the side of   **B** straight away from   **C** through   **D** across or over

_____ 8. Every arrested criminal, no matter how serious the crime, has a *right to* a fair trial.

   A fear of   **B** payment for   **C** suspicion of   **D** legal claim to

_____ **9.** We heard Anna *screech* when Preston scared the daylights out of her by jumping out of the shadows in the dark hallway.

    A scream   **B** giggle   **C** whisper   **D** faint

_____ **10.** Which *section* of the stadium would you like to sit in? I prefer the bleachers, but you may like the area that has chairs.

    A room   **B** seat   **C** row   **D** part

_____ **11.** When I dropped the light bulb on the concrete floor, the bulb *shattered*. I swept up all the pieces so no one would get hurt.

    A rolled   **B** broke   **C** collapsed   **D** bounced

_____ **12.** Yoshiko felt *supreme* joy when, to her surprise, she won first place in the contest.

    A ordinary   **B** familiar   **C** small   **D** great

_____ **13.** Your volleyball serves are always good, but I can't see how you're holding your hands. Can you show me your *technique* for serving?

    A score from   **B** way of   **C** reason for   **D** pride in

_____ **14.** I have been in a rowboat often, but sometime I would like to travel in the kind of *vessel* that can cross the ocean.

    A boat   **B** jet   **C** whale   **D** large building

_____ **15.** For an hour the children's eyes were big with excitement as Grandpa told them a *yarn* about his days as a cowboy.

    A joke   **B** story   **C** recipe   **D** nightmare

Vocabulary in Context

Name _____   Date _____

Crossword Puzzle

Read the clues and write the correct answers in the squares. There are several vocabulary words in this puzzle.

Across

1. One part
3. A story
5. A privilege or claim
8. Abbr. vice president
10. Past tense of eat
11. Short for Albert
12. Abbr. southwest
13. To receive in your hands something tossed or thrown
16. Quiet; unmoving
17. Conjunction that shows a choice between two things
18. Antonym of out
19. Not a part, but the whole amount
21. Best; greatest
23. Suffix added to associate to form association
24. Abbr. the people who call strikes and balls
26. Breaks and comes apart
27. Another name for Papa

Down

1. A scream
2. Abbr. New Jersey
3. Soon but not ___
4. Abbr. railroad
6. Present tense of went
7. Method
8. A ship
9. Side-by-side, like railroad tracks
14. Sticky black material used on roofs
15. A nonprofessional
17. Exclamation a person might utter when surprised
20. What clothing that is the right size does
22. Secondhand
25. That man

52

Name _____ Date _____

Standardized Test Practice

Circle the letter of the word that is closest in meaning to the capitalized word.

TIP

Always read all the answer choices. Many choices may make sense. Only one answer choice has the same or almost the same meaning as the capitalized word.

1. TECHNIQUE
   - **A** result
   - **B** method
   - **C** factor
   - **D** segment

2. SCREECH
   - **A** sob
   - **B** gasp
   - **C** whimper
   - **D** shriek

3. SHATTER
   - **A** hurry
   - **B** smash
   - **C** plunge
   - **D** drop

4. SUPREME
   - **A** serious
   - **B** wealthy
   - **C** true
   - **D** best

5. YARN
   - **A** tale
   - **B** needle
   - **C** summary
   - **D** mishap

6. OFFICER
   - **A** sailor
   - **B** professional
   - **C** leader
   - **D** worker

7. DEMAND
   - **A** insist
   - **B** tell
   - **C** demolish
   - **D** rush

8. SECTION
   - **A** blast
   - **B** segment
   - **C** square
   - **D** whole

9. INDIVIDUAL
   - **A** common
   - **B** weird
   - **C** unexpected
   - **D** personal

10. AMATEUR
    - **A** storyteller
    - **B** expert
    - **C** beginner
    - **D** worker

Vocabulary in Context

Vocabulary in Context G6, SV 9780547625799

Understanding Multiple-Meaning Words

Each box in this exercise contains a boldfaced word with its definitions. Read the definitions and then the sentences that use the word. Write the letter of the definition that applies to each sentence.

> **right**
> **a.** honest, moral, decent (adjective)
> **b.** correct, not mistaken (adjective)
> **c.** exactly (adverb)
> **d.** to fix or correct (verb)
> **e.** privilege or claim (noun)

_____ 1. Your answer to the last math problem is *right*.

_____ 2. In the United States, people have the *right* to say that they disagree with the government.

_____ 3. *Right* at twelve o'clock the factory whistle blew.

_____ 4. Can you *right* the spelling mistakes in your essay?

_____ 5. Brandon decided that telling his mother that he was the one who had lost the money was the *right* thing to do.

> **vessel**
> **a.** a bowl, pot, or other utensil made to hold things (noun)
> **b.** a ship (noun)
> **c.** a tube in the body through which blood or other fluids pass (noun)

_____ 6. Fat that builds up in blood *vessels* can cause heart disease.

_____ 7. Some *vessels* can carry cars across lakes or other bodies of water.

_____ 8. Beside the stove was a *vessel* filled with homemade dill pickles.

_____ 9. Our bodies contain an amazing system of *vessels*.

_____ 10. The thirsty laborer asked for a *vessel* of water.

Word Skills

Name _____ Date _____

Understanding Related Words

The words in the box can be related to the vocabulary words. See how many of the words you already know. Use the glossary to find the definitions of unfamiliar words.

technician	demanding	occasionally	technology	office
technical	locality	individualism	technicality	supremacy

Write the word from the box that best completes the meaning of the sentence.

_____ 1. If you're not familiar with a certain area, you might have trouble finding a street in that _____.

_____ 2. If you wish to talk with your principal, one place you would likely find her is in her _____.

_____ 3. In most parts of North America, rain does not come every day, but only _____.

_____ 4. Sarah is a very _____ child. She insists that I play with her all the time.

_____ 5. When they had beaten all their enemies, the people enjoyed their _____.

_____ 6. My brother is taking computer classes because he wants to get a job as a computer _____.

_____ 7. The criminal was released from the courtroom because of a legal _____ involving his trial.

_____ 8. My school places a high value on _____; students are encouraged to be themselves and pursue their own interests.

_____ 9. There have been great advances in computer _____ in the last decade. Computers get faster, smaller, and smarter every year.

_____ 10. The directions that came with my toy robot were filled with complicated _____ details; I had a hard time figuring out how to put together the robot.

Word Skills

Unit 5
Vocabulary in Context G6, SV 9780547625799

The Greek Word *techné*

The word *technique* and the related words *technical*, *technicality*, *technician*, *technocracy*, and *technology* come from the Greek noun *techné*, meaning "an art." Use a dictionary to learn the meanings and parts of speech of the five related words listed below. Then write the word from the box that best completes the meaning of each sentence below.

technical	technicality	technician	technocracy	technology

_____ 1. Because my dad knows a lot about computers, he understands computer books that contain _____ language.

_____ 2. What would it be like if our democracy were replaced by a _____? I wonder if society's problems would be solved more easily.

_____ 3. Do you think someday we will have the _____ that will make it possible for us to live on a different planet?

_____ 4. The _____ told me to hold still while she took an X-ray of my arm.

_____ 5. Janelle said she understood most of the lecture, but she asked the speaker to explain one _____.

_____ 6. We won the game because of a _____; the other team had too many players on the field.

_____ 7. Our school just hired a computer _____ to help take care of the computer lab.

_____ 8. A society based on technical government control is called a _____.

_____ 9. What kinds of advancements in _____ can you imagine will occur in the next century?

_____ 10. The sound effects during the play were distorted because of _____ difficulties with the sound system.

Word Skills

Writing

Imagine you are a sailor on a ship like the *Artful Dodger*. Write a short yarn describing one of your exciting adventures. Use some of the vocabulary words from this unit in your story.

_____

_____

_____

_____

_____

_____

_____

_____

_____

_____

_____

_____

_____

Writing

Gold!

Read the selection. Think about the meanings of the **boldfaced** words. Then go back to the selection. Underline the words or sentences that give you a clue to the meaning of each **boldfaced** word.

January 24, 1848, was just another workday for carpenter James Marshall. He was building a sawmill for John Sutter. Sutter owned a portion of land on the American River in California. Bending down, Marshall saw something glitter in the water. To his surprise, it was several nuggets of gold.

Word of the discovery of gold spread quickly. Gold fever was like an **epidemic**. But it was not a spreading sickness. From near and far, hopeful people rushed to California in **anticipation** of striking it rich. On February 28, 1849, the first ship full of gold seekers arrived in San Francisco. They, and the thousands who followed them, were called "forty-niners."

The **craze** for gold drove people in the East to give up good jobs and rush westward to find their fortune. Once they arrived, the miners used a pan or a sifter called a cradle to find nuggets in streams or rivers. They rocked water and gravel back and forth in the cradle. This sifted out the lighter sand and left any gold in the bottom. Some traced the gold to its source in the mountains and used **dynamite** to blow it out.

Many miners lived in **shanties**, run-down shacks built quickly and crudely. Their lives were **solitary** and often lonely. Miners **distrusted** one another, so they seldom worked together. They were afraid that someone would cheat them out of the gold they had worked so hard to find.

Those who did strike it rich often rushed to town to spend their money freely. Many more miners, however, found no gold and returned home **empty-handed**. Some gave up because of **homesickness** and went back to the places they had left. But many people who did not find gold stayed in California anyway. They settled on **homesteads**, where they raised cattle or farmed. When the California Gold Rush ended, it left behind few millionaires. But it had produced a young and growing state.

Context Clues

In each sentence a word or phrase is underlined. Choose a word from the box to replace that word or phrase. Write the word on the line.

anticipation	epidemic	empty-handed	dynamite	homesickness
shanties	distrusted	craze	homesteads	solitary

1. News of the discovery of gold was like a <u>rapidly spreading outbreak</u> of the measles.

   _____

2. In 1849, over 80,000 people headed west to find gold in California with <u>eager expectation</u>.

   _____

3. The popular, short-lived <u>madness</u> for gold became known as the gold rush.

   _____

4. Some miners used <u>an explosive</u> to blow up the mountains and get at the rock that contained the gold.

   _____

5. When not digging or blowing up mountains, miners lived in <u>run-down shacks</u> made of wood.

   _____.

6. A gold miner led a <u>lonely and private</u> life, keeping away from other miners.

   _____

7. The miners <u>did not trust</u> each other and were afraid of being cheated or robbed.

   _____

8. After months or years of work, many miners found no gold and went home <u>having gained nothing</u>.

   _____

9. One reason that many miners gave up the search for gold was <u>a longing for home and family</u>.

   _____

10. Though few struck it rich, many were given <u>land to farm, improve, and eventually own</u>.

    _____

Word Groups

Read each group of words and think about how they are alike. Write the word from the box that completes each group.

anticipation	craze	shanties	dynamite

1. madness, enthusiasm, _____

2. explosive, gunpowder, _____

3. huts, dwellings, _____

4. hope, looking forward to, _____

Vocabulary in Context

Word Origins

Knowing the origin of a word can help you understand its meaning. Read each word origin. Then write each word from the box next to its origin.

homestead	epidemic	dynamite	solitary	distrust	anticipation

1. from Latin solus, alone _____

2. from Greek dynamikos, powerful _____

3. from Old English hāmstede, property _____

4. from Greek epi, among + demos, people _____

5. from Latin anticipāt(us) + ion, taken before _____

6. from dis, not + German trost, comfort _____

Cloze Paragraph

Use the words in the box to complete the paragraph. Then reread it to make sure it makes sense.

distrusted	empty-handed	anticipation	solitary
craze	homesickness	shanties	

The (1) _____ for gold brought so many families into California that in 1850 it

became a state. This started other gold rushes. In 1859, in (2) _____ of striking it

rich, people moved to Colorado with the Pikes Peak gold rush. The gold seekers appeared and built

(3) _____. The miners lived their (4) _____ lives and

faced (5) _____. The miners at Pikes Peak (6) _____ other

miners, too. And just as before, some found riches while others left (7) _____.

Vocabulary in Context

Name _____   Date _____

Word Riddle

Write each word from the box next to its definition. Then write the boxed letters in order in the blanks at the bottom. You will find the answer to this riddle: What did the miner call his barely furnished shack?

epidemic	shanties	empty-handed	craze	anticipation
distrusted	homesteads	dynamite	homesickness	solitary

1. a popular, short-lived madness ___ ___ [ ] ___ ___

2. lacked trust or confidence in ___ ___ ___ ___ ___ ___ ___ [ ] ___ ___ ___

3. sudden spread of an idea or disease ___ ___ ___ ___ ___ ___ ___ [ ]

4. the act of expecting ___ ___ ___ ___ ___ [ ] ___ ___ ___ ___ ___

5. blasting explosive ___ ___ [ ] ___ ___ ___ ___ ___

6. being away from people; alone ___ ___ ___ ___ [ ] ___ ___ [ ]

7. condition of missing one's home or family ___ ___ ___ [ ] ___ ___ ___ ___ ___ ___ ___ ___

8. land given to people to work and improve [ ] ___ ___ ___ ___ ___ [ ] ___ ___

9. broken-down shacks ___ ___ ___ [ ] ___ ___ ___

10. having nothing ___ ___ [ ][ ] ___ ___ ___ ___ ___

Answer: ____   ___ ___ ___ ___ ___ ___   ___ ___ ___ ___ ___ ___ !

Vocabulary in Context G6, SV 9780547625799

Vocabulary in Context

Yes or No?

Read each question. For a "yes" answer, write *yes* on the line. For a "no" answer, write *no* on the line and write a sentence that gives the correct meaning of the underlined word.

epidemic	shanties	empty-handed	craze	anticipation
distrusted	homesteads	dynamite	homesickness	solitary

1. Does a craze usually last for a very long time?

   _____

2. Are shanties built to provide long-term shelter?

   _____

3. Would you keep secrets from a person you distrusted?

   _____

4. If you use dynamite, are you covering something in water?

   _____

5. If you did not win a prize, did you leave the contest empty-handed?

   _____

6. Were homesteads given to farmers and ranchers?

   _____

7. If your family lives nearby, are you likely to suffer from homesickness?

   _____

8. Do you feel a sense of anticipation about something that has happened?

   _____

9. Does a person with many friends live a solitary life?

   _____

10. Is an epidemic a single, isolated case of an illness?

   _____

Name _____ Date _____

Standardized Test Practice

Read the sentences. Look for the best word to use to complete the sentence. Circle the letter for your choice.

> **TIP**
> Before you choose an answer, try reading the sentences with each answer choice. This will help you choose an answer that makes sense.

1. Everyone has gold rush fever. The _____ is spreading.
   A medicine   **B** dynamite   **C** epidemic   **D** gold

2. I would not like to live alone. I don't care for a _____ life.
   A long   **B** solitary   **C** hungry   **D** supreme

3. The store was out of everything. We went home _____.
   A satisfied   **B** solitary   **C** empty-handed   **D** underwater

4. The miners blasted the mountains with explosives. They used _____.
   A homesteads   **B** tools   **C** horses   **D** dynamite

5. People dreamed of gold. They were willing to risk everything in _____ of striking it rich.
   A anticipation   **B** destruction   **C** dynamite   **D** fear

6. He kept everything to himself. He _____ everyone.
   A married   **B** distrusted   **C** paid   **D** trusted

7. She missed her family. She had a case of _____.
   A homesickness   **B** homesteads   **C** books   **D** dynamite

8. Look at the broken-down shacks. Those _____ are deserted.
   A homesteads   **B** shanties   **C** prices   **D** boards

9. People were given land to farm. They lived on _____.
   A mountains   **B** homesickness   **C** livestock   **D** homesteads

10. What will be the next popular, short-lived madness? No one can guess the next _____.
    A story   **B** epidemic   **C** craze   **D** condition

True or False

Decide whether each statement is true (**T**) or false (**F**) based on the meaning of the word in italics. Write *T* or *F* on each line. Use the glossary or a dictionary if you need help.

_____ 1. A *resident* of California could live in Colorado.

_____ 2. Many health problems result from getting *sufficient* amounts of nutrients and fresh foods.

_____ 3. She loves being a *dynamiter* because she finds working with explosives very exciting.

_____ 4. Most people don't care about things that are *meaningful* to them.

_____ 5. If you are *distrustful* of someone, you do not want to be his or her best friend.

_____ 6. Careful studying is a good *strategy* for doing well on exams.

_____ 7. You can make soup in a *fragment* of a pot.

_____ 8. Buses are used to *conduct* passengers from one place to another.

_____ 9. A happy celebration is an example of a *crisis*.

_____ 10. You must follow the steps of a *process* in exact order if you hope to achieve good results.

Now rewrite each false sentence so that it shows the correct meaning of the word in italics.

_____

_____

_____

_____

_____

_____

_____

Word Skills

Questions and Answers

Answer each of the following questions in one sentence. Use the italicized words in your sentences.

1. What is a good *strategy* for getting to school on time?

   _____

2. What was the cause of a *crisis* you have heard or read about?

   _____

3. If you were going to *conduct* some foreign students on a tour of your town, what would you show them first?

   _____

4. What would you do with a *fragment* of a meteorite if you found one?

   _____

5. What is the most *meaningful* book, story, or article you ever read? What made it so meaningful?

   _____

6. Give an example of a *process* you could teach to others.

   _____

7. How do others know that you are a *distrustful* person?

   _____

8. Would you enjoy doing the job of a *dynamiter*?

   _____

9. Of what community are you a *resident*?

   _____

10. How much sleep at night do you believe is a *sufficient* amount?

    _____

Word Skills

Suffix *-ful*

The suffix *-ful* means "full of" or "likely to." It can be added to many English words. In most cases, when you add *-ful* to a base word, you form an adjective.

Add *-ful* to the words in italics listed below. (Notice that the *-ful* ending has only one *l*.) Then use the new word you have created in a sentence.

1. full of *meaning* = _____

_____

2. full of *pain* = _____

_____

3. full of *wonder* = _____

_____

4. likely to *help* = _____

_____

5. likely to *forget* = _____

_____

Latin Root *duct*

The Latin root *duct* means "lead." The word *conduct* contains this root and comes from the Latin word *conducere*, which is made up of *con-*, meaning "together," and *ducere*, meaning "to lead."

All the words in the box also contain the *duct* root. Use a dictionary to learn the part of speech and meaning(s) of each word. Then write the word from the box that best completes the meaning of each sentence.

abduct	deduct	induct	introduction	product

1. Should we _____ Carol as president of the Spanish club?

2. That game is the most popular _____ that our store sells.

3. The kidnappers were caught before they could _____ their target.

4. No one made a(n) _____, so I have no idea who that person is.

5. Adam just gave you five dollars, so you should _____ that from what he still owes you.

Word Skills

Writing

Imagine you are a miner during the gold rush of 1849. You are in a mining camp living in a shanty near the American River in California. You have been there for several months, but you have not yet found gold. How do you feel about your life there? Are your hopes for finding gold still high?

Write a letter to a friend back east telling what your life is like and how you feel about it. Also tell how you pan for gold. Use some vocabulary words from this unit in your writing.

August 1849

Dear _____,

_____

_____

_____

_____

_____

_____

_____

_____

_____

_____

_____

Writing

A Man of Vision

Read the selection. Think about the meanings of the **boldfaced** words. Then go back to the selection. Underline the words or sentences that give you a clue to the meaning of each **boldfaced** word.

Benjamin Franklin was a remarkable man. Read about some of his amazing inventions!

Almost everyone believes that Ben Franklin flew a kite in a thunderstorm. According to the story, lightning struck his kite and made sparks fly from a key that he had tied to the string. Also according to the story, people thought that flying a kite in a lightning storm was **ludicrous**. They believed that Ben was crazy to attempt such a dangerous feat. People were, at first, **skeptical** of Ben's unusual ideas. They didn't believe that his ideas could ever amount to anything important. They eventually learned, however, that Ben's **intellectual** strengths gave him the ability to create new and exciting inventions.

It is not always easy for inventors to get people to **comprehend** their new ideas. This must have been true for Ben Franklin. He was full of many **progressive** ideas.

Supposedly Franklin flew a kite to **illustrate** that lightning is electricity. Even though he did not do the experiment with the kite, he did learn that lightning is electricity. He used what he had learned to invent the lightning rod. This simple metal rod was attached to a roof. His **prediction** that lightning would travel down the rod to the ground and save a building from catching fire was correct. Everyone could **benefit** from his idea.

Franklin made many other **contributions** to help people in his community. He made **bifocal** glasses that had two kinds of lenses to enable people to see better. He made a stove that saved fuel and heated a room better than others. He never did **patent** his inventions to stop others from stealing his ideas.

We benefit today from Franklin's wish to help others. In Philadelphia, he **established** the police and fire departments. He also started a public library, university, and hospital. Next time you check the mailbox, remember that Franklin was the **founder** of the U.S. Postal Service.

Perhaps Benjamin Franklin's most **significant** contribution was helping create the United States. He signed both the Declaration of Independence and the Constitution.

Ben Franklin was truly a **visionary**—a man with an eye to the future. He made many contributions, not only as an inventor, but also as a public servant and statesman.

Vocabulary in Context G6, SV 9780547625799

Name _____ Date _____

Context Clues

Read each sentence. Look for clues to help you complete each sentence with a word from the box. Write the word on the line.

prediction	established	comprehend	significant
progressive	bifocal	founder	benefit
patent	ludicrous	intellectual	skeptical

1. When people think about the number and variety of Benjamin Franklin's contributions, they can't quite _____ how he did it.

2. Some of Franklin's inventions seemed strange to some people, and they were _____ that the inventions would work.

3. Many people even thought that his ideas were _____, and they thought he was crazy.

4. He didn't care about protecting the rights to his ideas in order to prevent them from being stolen, so he didn't _____ his inventions.

5. His _____, or forward-thinking, ideas continue to help people today in areas of government, science, and public services.

6. Franklin's invention of _____ glasses, in which two lenses were put together to help people see better, was another great idea.

7. Perhaps Franklin's most _____ contribution had to do with the creation of our nation.

8. He was a signer of the Declaration of Independence, which _____ the colonies' freedom from England.

9. The country continued to _____, or gain, from Franklin's wisdom and help in shaping the Constitution in 1787.

10. Franklin's _____ that the new nation would survive all its problems has certainly come true.

11. Along with George Washington, Benjamin Franklin can be considered a _____ of the United States.

12. After people learned that his inventions were really useful, they realized that he had great _____ capabilities.

Word Maze

All the words in the list below are hidden in the maze. The words are arranged forward, backward, up, and down. Put a circle around each word as you find it and cross the word off the list. Different words may overlap and use the same letter.

prediction	illustrate	established	comprehend	significant
progressive	bifocal	founder	benefit	patent
ludicrous	intellectual	skeptical	contributions	visionary

Vocabulary in Context

```
E  T  A  R  T  S  U  L  L  I  B  O  Q  C  N  E  Q
M  B  E  N  E  F  I  T  J  Z  O  F  P  O  B  L  F
C  Q  O  L  D  O  G  S  Z  G  T  J  Y  N  A  V  D
O  T  L  L  D  P  N  A  L  H  V  N  Y  T  P  R  C
B  A  A  X  N  R  Y  J  A  X  I  X  W  R  A  T  K
T  Q  U  M  E  O  Y  P  C  F  S  N  Y  I  T  Q  T
N  P  T  C  H  G  W  W  O  D  I  N  D  B  E  S  B
A  R  C  N  E  R  O  S  F  M  O  G  C  U  N  J  W
C  E  E  E  R  E  S  C  I  Z  N  V  K  T  T  N  I
I  D  L  S  P  S  J  A  B  O  A  Z  F  I  G  R  E
F  I  L  M  M  S  Z  J  Y  N  R  Q  Q  O  W  B  X
I  C  E  X  O  I  F  I  Y  F  Y  V  Z  N  P  C  R
N  T  T  U  C  V  I  K  S  W  T  Z  K  S  N  S  B
G  I  N  H  D  E  H  S  I  L  B  A  T  S  E  A  O
I  O  I  N  K  O  M  F  O  U  N  D  E  R  F  B  E
S  N  U  B  A  S  H  S  U  O  R  C  I  D  U  L  I
K  I  N  O  R  Y  X  S  K  E  P  T  I  C  A  L  U
```

Tangled-up Words

A word is underlined in each sentence below. The word sounds similar to a word in the box. Its meaning makes it the wrong word for the sentence.

Read the paragraphs. Find the word in the box that should replace the underlined word. Write the word on the line next to the number of the underlined word.

prediction	illustrate	established	comprehend	significant
visionary	progressive	bifocal	founder	contributions
benefit	patent	ludicrous	intellectual	skeptical

If I had lived in the days of Ben Franklin, I most likely would not have been able to (1) complicate what he was trying to do with a metal rod attached to the top of a barn roof. I would have thought, "This man is crazy. That is a (2) lucrative idea." I'm sure that I, along with many other people at that time, would have been (3) spectacle that his idea would work. Later, when I learned what he had discovered, I would have understood that his invention was a very (4) magnificent one. He was able to (5) irritate with this experiment that lightning contains electricity, which can cause fires. His (6) preparation that lightning would travel down the rod proved to be correct. His invention of the lightning rod could save a barn or other building from catching fire. People certainly did (7) misfit from it!

Franklin (8) distinguished many important things in his community, such as the police and fire departments and a public library. I am particularly impressed with his invention of the (9) bicycle glasses. I am also impressed that he was the (10) flounder of the U.S. Postal Service. He was quite an (11) invisible man.

Although the time of Ben Franklin must have been very exciting, I'm glad I live today so that I can enjoy the results of all Franklin's work. I can look back and see how (12) protective his ideas were for his time. I can say that I'll never quite understand why he didn't (13) satin his inventions. I can also say that I'm glad he was such a great inventor, public servant, and (14) visible. We will always be grateful to him for all of his (15) constitutions.

1. _____   6. _____   11. _____

2. _____   7. _____   12. _____

3. _____   8. _____   13. _____

4. _____   9. _____   14. _____

5. _____   10. _____   15. _____

Name _____ Date _____

Standardized Test Practice

Circle the letter of the word that best completes each sentence.

TIP

Before you choose an answer, try reading the sentences with each answer choice. This will help you choose an answer that makes sense.

Vocabulary in Context

1. The teacher showed a picture to _____ his point.
   A patent   B illustrate   C confuse   D change

2. It is wise to _____ your inventions so no one can steal them.
   A modify   B patent   C destroy   D donate

3. We did not _____ the size of the problem.
   A comprehend   B allow   C illustrate   D record

4. The man saw more clearly after he put on his _____ glasses.
   A colorful   B significant   C progress   D bifocal

5. Early settlers _____ our town in 1750.
   A destroyed   B established   C encouraged   D delivered

6. Everyone can _____ from Ben Franklin's inventions.
   A founder   B benefit   C illustrate   D compare

7. Our new mayor has clever and _____ ideas.
   A progressive   B stale   C predictable   D uncaring

8. The _____ of our school spoke to the graduates.
   A terminator   B founder   C pretender   D pilot

9. The scientist's _____ later proved to be correct.
   A washed   B retorted   C prediction   D office

10. I believe that my friend is a _____ because she always imagines fantastic ways to improve our world.

    A neighbor   **B** teacher   **C** performer   **D** visionary

11. My brother is very _____, and he loves to read and study.

    A friendly   **B** grouchy   **C** stubborn   **D** intellectual

12. I thought that my friend's idea to jump off the roof for fun was _____.

    A significant   **B** ludicrous   **C** special   **D** important

13. My mother was _____ when I told her that I had cleaned my room without being told.

    A skeptical   **B** angry   **C** patient   **D** bored

14. Our class brought in many _____ for the community food drive.

    A answers   **B** contributions   **C** predictions   **D** bicycles

15. The cell phone has seen _____ improvements over the last twenty years.

    A foolish   **B** significant   **C** disturbing   **D** subconscious

Vocabulary in Context

Name _____ Date _____

Understanding Multiple-Meaning Words

The words in the box have more than one definition. Look for clues in each sentence to tell which definition is being used. Write the letter of the definition that applies to each sentence.

---

established
a. set up on a lasting basis (verb)
b. showed beyond a doubt; proved (verb)

progressive
a. forward thinking (adjective)
b. developing or advancing in seriousness (adjective)

benefit
a. to receive good or gain from (verb)
b. a performance to raise money for a cause (noun)

illustrate
a. to make clear or explain by giving examples (verb)
b. to show something in a picture, drawing, or diagram (verb)

Word Skills

_____ **1.** The lawyer *established* that the man was guilty by presenting evidence about his crime.

_____ **2.** Franklin *established* the police and fire departments within the community of Philadelphia.

_____ **3.** Franklin had more *progressive* ideas than most other people.

_____ **4.** Marcos was diagnosed with a *progressive* disease, so his symptoms will continue to get worse until he can be cured.

_____ **5.** Our community is hosting a *benefit* concert to raise funds for college scholarships.

_____ **6.** We can all *benefit* from Ben Franklin's clever ideas.

_____ **7.** Franklin's inventions *illustrate* his concerns for other people.

_____ **8.** I will write the story and my sister, who is an artist, will *illustrate* it.

Synonyms

Write the letter of the word or words that are closest in meaning to the capitalized word.

_____ **1.** SIGNIFICANCE

    A protest   **B** importance   **C** danger   **D** attendance

_____ **2.** COMPREHENSION

    A understanding   **B** question   **C** discussion   **D** trade

_____ **3.** ESTABLISH

    A to enjoy   **B** to disturb   **C** to create   **D** to challenge

_____ **4.** PREDICT

    A to model   **B** to move   **C** to escape   **D** to forecast

_____ **5.** ILLUSTRATION

    A demonstration   **B** engagement   **C** deletion   **D** transferral

_____ **6.** PROGRESSION

    A historical   **B** backward   **C** advancement   **D** unusual

_____ **7.** BINOCULARS

    A single-vision   **B** double-telescope   **C** simple   **D** steady

_____ **8.** FOUND

    A to present   **B** to create   **C** to explore   **D** to guide

_____ **9.** BENEFICIAL

    A advantageous   **B** interesting   **C** shrinkage   **D** critical

_____ **10.** INTELLECT

    A intelligence   **B** laziness   **C** challenge   **D** strength

_____ **11.** SKEPTIC

    A one who doubts   **B** one who bores   **C** one who amuses   **D** one who cures

_____ **12.** VISION

    A founder   **B** sight   **C** creation   **D** hearing

Word Skills

The Suffix –ion

The suffix –ion, when added to a verb, means "the act or process of." If the word *magnify* means "to make something look larger," the word *magnification* means "the process of making something look larger."

Match each word on the left with its definition on the right. Write the letter of the definition on the line.

_____ 1. contribution

_____ 2. exploration

_____ 3. completion

_____ 4. prediction

_____ 5. concentration

_____ 6. participation

_____ 7. expression

_____ 8. comprehension

_____ 9. observation

_____ 10. calculation

a. the act of foretelling the future

b. the act of taking part in an event or activity

c. the act of focusing one's attention on a task

d. the act of understanding

e. the act of watching

f. the act of putting into words

g. the act of figuring out using math

h. the process of finishing

i. the act of making payments to a cause

j. the act of traveling in unfamiliar territory to discover new things

Word Pairs

Words with similar parts have related meanings. Study each word pair. Think about how the meanings are alike. Then write a sentence for each word.

1. skeptic—skeptical

_____

_____

2. intellect—intellectual

_____

_____

3. illustrate—illustration

_____

_____

Word Skills

Writing

Inventing something can be very exciting and rewarding. What would you like to invent and patent? Would it be something to ride in, a new kind of telephone, or perhaps a new kind of game?

Write a paragraph telling about your invention. Give it a name, tell how it works, and explain its uses. Use some vocabulary words from this unit in your writing.

_____

_____

_____

_____

_____

_____

_____

_____

_____

_____

_____

Writing

Faces in Stone

Read the selection. Think about the meanings of the **boldfaced** words. Then go back to the selection. Underline the words or sentences that give you a clue to the meaning of each **boldfaced** word.

When **sculptor** Gutzon Borglum first **beheld** Mount Rushmore in the Black Hills of South Dakota, he knew he was looking at the place where he would carve his greatest work of art. "United States history shall march along that skyline!" he said.

And march it did, in the shape of four **renowned** U.S. presidents. Borglum's sculpture on the face of the mountain shows the **bust** of George Washington. Washington's head and shoulders stand as high as a five-story building. Next to Washington are **carvings** of Thomas Jefferson, Abraham Lincoln, and Theodore Roosevelt.

The place for the Mount Rushmore Memorial was chosen in 1925. Borglum said then it would take seven years to create the artwork. In fact, the sculpture took twice that time.

Many problems slowed the progress. Right away, the start on the memorial was delayed two years for lack of money. The work was also difficult. Each of the heads was cut out of the granite cliff atop Mount Rushmore's **summit**. Borglum's crew used explosives and drills to shape the four faces on this highest point of the mountain. Sometimes mistakes were made. One big error was made in cutting Jefferson's head. It had to be blasted away and a new one begun.

Throughout the project, Borglum was **assisted** by his son, Lincoln. The boy was 12 when he started helping. He was a man of 26 when he put the finishing touches on the sculpture, just a few months after his father's death. The mighty efforts of the two Borglums had created a magnificent sculpture. The **majestic** heads of the presidents stand 60 feet tall. They make up the world's largest sculpture.

Unlike many memorials, there is no **inscription** on Mount Rushmore. Time has shown that this exciting artwork needs no words to describe it. These **dramatic** faces from U.S. history speak for themselves.

Name _____   Date _____

Context Clues

In each sentence a word or phrase is underlined. Choose a word from the box to replace that word or phrase. Write the word on the line.

renowned	sculptor	majestic	inscription	beheld
carvings	dramatic	assisted	bust	summit

1. Each year, many tourists come to see the <u>sculptures</u> at Mount Rushmore.

   _____

2. On the left side of Mount Rushmore is a sculpture showing the <u>head and shoulders</u> of George Washington.

   _____

3. Other carvings include the <u>famous</u> United States presidents Thomas Jefferson, Abraham Lincoln, and Theodore Roosevelt.

   _____

4. These giant stone sculptures are a <u>grand and impressive</u> sight.

   _____

5. The four presidents look out over the land from the <u>peak</u> of the mountain.

   _____

6. The <u>person who carved the sculptures</u>, Gutzon Borglum, first saw Mount Rushmore in 1924.

   _____

7. Borglum first <u>observed</u> the huge mountain and knew that this was the place for his work.

   _____

8. Calvin Coolidge, president when the first cutting of the rock began, had hoped to have an <u>engraved message</u> that could be read from three miles away.

   _____

9. Coolidge gave a very <u>exciting</u> speech before Borglum drilled the first holes in the stone.

   _____

10. Many workers <u>helped</u> in the task of creating the massive stone sculptures over a period of fourteen years.

   _____

Unit 8
Vocabulary in Context G6, SV 9780547625799

Vocabulary in Context

Name _____   Date _____

Word Groups

Read each pair of words. Think about how they are alike. Write the word from the box that best completes each group.

beheld	assisted	renowned	summit
dramatic	majestic	bust	

Vocabulary in Context

1. top, peak, _____

2. famous, well-known, _____

3. observed, viewed, _____

4. splendid, grand, _____

5. exciting, theatrical, _____

6. sculpture, figure, _____

Analogies

An **analogy** compares two pairs of words. The relationship between the first pair of words is the same as the relationship between the second pair of words. Use the words in the box to complete the following analogies.

renowned	bust	sculptor
inscription	summit	carvings

1. *Drawings* are to *pictures* as _____ are to *sculptures*.

2. *Song* is to *recording* as _____ is to *writing*.

3. *Violinist* is to *violin* as _____ is to *sculpture*.

4. *Statue* is to *whole* as _____ is to *part*.

5. *Floor* is to *bottom* as _____ is to *top*.

6. *Popular* is to *well-liked* as _____ is to *famous*.

Crossword Puzzle

Use the clues and the words in the box to complete the crossword puzzle.

beheld	sculptor	carvings	assisted	inscription
bust	summit	majestic	dramatic	renowned

Across

2. stately, grand
8. gave aid to
9. carved message
10. theatrical, exciting

Down

1. looked at
3. sculptures
4. person who carves sculptures
5. sculpture showing head and shoulders
6. well-known
7. highest point of a mountain

Yes or No?

Read each question. For a "yes" answer, write *yes* on the line. For a "no" answer, write *no* on the line and write a sentence that gives the correct meaning of the underlined word.

1. Is a sculptor usually known for his paintings?

_____

2. Does a dramatic performance bore the audience?

_____

3. Does a bust show a person's whole body?

_____

4. If you reach the summit, have you climbed to the top?

_____

5. Is an inscription usually a drawing?

_____

6. If you beheld a rainbow, did you imagine it?

_____

7. Could you make carvings that lasted for years?

_____

8. Would you describe something majestic as common and everyday?

_____

9. If someone assisted you, did they get in your way?

_____

10. Do lots of people know about you if you are renowned?

_____

www.harcourtschoolsupply.com
© HMH Supplemental Publishers Inc. All rights reserved.

Vocabulary in Context

Standardized Test Practice

Read each sentence carefully. Then choose the best answer to complete each sentence. Circle the letter of the answer you have chosen.

> **TIP**
>
> Think about the meaning of the boldfaced word. Don't be fooled by a word that looks similar to the boldfaced word.

1. **Carvings** are _____.
   A toys   B cards   C sculptures   D paintings

2. The **bust** of a sculpture shows the _____.
   A full body   B rust   C feet   D head and shoulders

3. The **summit** of Mount Rushmore is its _____.
   A bottom   B peak   C summer   D slope

4. A **sculptor** is a _____.
   A carver   B singer   C catcher   D president

5. People who are **renowned** are _____.
   A unknown   B nasty   C famous   D restless

6. Something **majestic** is _____.
   A impressive   B small   C many-sided   D old

7. When I **beheld** the mountain, I _____ it.
   A believed   B observed   C carved   D bought

8. A **dramatic** speech is _____.
   A ridiculous   B sad   C exciting   D dreamy

9. An **inscription** is a _____.
   A grocery store B pill   C description   D carved message

10. When the workers **assisted** Borglum, they _____ him.
    A asked   B helped   C hired   D left

83

Vocabulary in Context

True or False

Decide whether each statement is true or false based on the meaning of the word in italics. Write *T* or *F* on each line. Use the glossary or a dictionary if you need help.

_____ **1.** Tourists often visit a historical *site* such as Mount Rushmore.

_____ **2.** By the time you are old, you will have gained much *experience*.

_____ **3.** Advertisers try to *persuade* us to buy things.

_____ **4.** A dog can often be a good *companion*.

_____ **5.** If you don't want to listen to the sales call on the phone, you might *interrupt* the caller.

_____ **6.** To *abandon* all hope means to continue to believe something good will happen.

_____ **7.** A hungry snake is likely to *pursue* a mouse.

_____ **8.** Gutzon Borglum *predicted* that it would take him exactly seven years to create the artwork for Mount Rushmore.

_____ **9.** A traveler making *progress* is getting further and further from his destination.

_____ **10.** You will immediately forget a meeting with a *remarkable* person.

Now rewrite each false sentence so that it shows the correct meaning of the word in italics.

_____

_____

_____

_____

_____

_____

Word Skills

Synonyms

Write the letter of the word that is closest in meaning to the capitalized word.

_____ **1.** ABANDON

    A to stay   **B** to desert   **C** to oppose   **D** to assault

_____ **2.** COMPANION

    A buddy   **B** stranger   **C** victim   **D** explorer

_____ **3.** SITE

    A vision   **B** place   **C** home   **D** castle

_____ **4.** INTERRUPT

    A to listen   **B** to speak   **C** to stop   **D** to determine

_____ **5.** EXPERIENCE

    A knowledge   **B** wit   **C** age   **D** power

_____ **6.** PREDICTED

    A declared   **B** foretold   **C** expected   **D** remembered

_____ **7.** PROGRESS

    A delay   **B** excitement   **C** fortune   **D** advancement

_____ **8.** PURSUE

    A to retreat   **B** to disguise   **C** to follow   **D** to fight

_____ **9.** REMARKABLE

    A common   **B** likable   **C** sincere   **D** extraordinary

_____ **10.** PERSUADE

    A to enrage   **B** to conceal   **C** to convince   **D** to frighten

Word Skills

    Vocabulary in Context G6, SV 9780547625799

Name _____   Date _____

The Prefix *pro-*

The prefix pro- has several meanings, including "before" *(prologue)*, "forward" or "ahead" *(propel)*, and "in favor of" *(pro-sports.)* The word *progress* comes from the Latin *pro-*, meaning "before," and *gradi*, meaning "to step."

All the words in the box also contain the prefix *pro-*. Use a dictionary to learn the part of speech and meaning(s) of each word. Then write the word from the box that best completes the meaning of each sentence.

proceed	profess	promote	protect	provide

1. In addition to wearing a helmet, what else can you do to _____ yourself when skateboarding?

2. "Please _____ to the nearest exit," said the flight attendant calmly.

3. As the hostess, Carmen will _____ all the food for the party, but she asked that we bring our favorite dance music.

4. In math class, David will often _____ to know the answer, but I have found that he is frequently wrong.

5. Mr. Perales will _____ Linda to be the manager because she is such a hard worker.

6. I would _____ my knowledge of what happened in the hallway, but I wasn't actually there.

7. Before he could _____ with the interview, the reporter had to get all the questions approved by the star's agent.

8. The school hopes to _____ a healthy lifestyle for students by providing only water and juice in the vending machines.

Writing

People who have seen Mount Rushmore are struck by the size and grandness of the sculptures. With a few well-chosen words, you can create a poem about it. Look back at the picture of Mount Rushmore. What words come to mind? How does it make you feel?

Write a poem that expresses your thoughts and feelings. Follow the directions for each line of the poem. You can also get some ideas from the sample poem below. Use some vocabulary words from this unit in your writing.

Sample:

The subject (noun):	Mount Rushmore
Two adjectives:	sculptured, stately
Three verbs:	watching, listening, protecting
Four words naming feelings:	pride, excitement, admiration, wonder
One or two words to replace the subject in the first line:	stone faces

Subject: _____

Adjectives: _____

Verbs: _____

Feelings: _____

Replace the subject: _____

87

Writing

For the Glory of Zeus

Read the selection. Think about the meanings of the **boldfaced** words. Then go back to the selection. Underline the words or sentences that give you a clue to the meaning of each **boldfaced** word.

The next time you watch an Olympic race, think about Coroebus. This young runner was the first Olympic winner on record. He won a two-hundred-meter race held near a place called Olympia, in Greece. That was three thousand years ago.

The Olympic games were started as a part of a religious ceremony, a **tribute** to the chief Greek god, Zeus. They were held every four years. At first, there was only one event, the race that Coroebus won. People came from neighboring villages to sit on the grass and watch. Later, a **stadium** was built. Then the runners competed in this enclosed, roofless area.

As the games became more popular, more events were added. These included chariot races and the pentathlon. This five-event contest featured running, jumping, wrestling, throwing the discus, and throwing the **javelin**, or spear.

At the height of the games in ancient Greece, **attendance** was in the tens of thousands. Only men could go to the games. Women were not permitted to watch, and any found at the games could be put to death. The men at the Olympics came from all over the Greek world. During times of war, they would **proclaim** a truce during and just after the games. With peace declared, men could travel without fear.

Then, as now, the athletes underwent **strenuous** training. Every day they worked out under the stern eyes of their coaches. Participants were also very **competitive**. Winning was everything. It was the **supreme** achievement. No prizes were given for second or third place. Losers walked away in shame.

With great **pomp** and splendor, each winning player was marched to the Temple of Zeus. There, the **contestant** received his prize, a wreath from the sacred olive tree. But the most important prize for an Olympic athlete was the honor of being the best, earned through great skill and effort.

Vocabulary in Context G6, SV 9780547625799

Context Clues

For each sentence write the letter of the word or phrase that is closest in meaning to the word or words in italics. Use context clues to help you choose the correct answer.

_____ 1. The Greeks honored Zeus, their chief god, by *paying tribute to* him through athletic events at Olympic games.

     A honoring   **B** illustrating   **C** ignoring   **D** challenging

_____ 2. The Olympic events required a lot of energy; in fact, they were so *strenuous* that only the strongest and most skilled competitors had even a small chance to win.

     A dangerous   **B** difficult   **C** entertaining   **D** popular

_____ 3. The athletes competed in an enclosed area, a roofless building called a *stadium*.

     A foundation   **B** meadow   **C** coliseum   **D** temple

_____ 4. The Olympic games became so popular that the stadium was always filled, with *attendance* in the tens of thousands.

     A challengers   **B** students   **C** players   **D** spectators

_____ 5. People's everyday lives were ordinary, so they loved the excitement created by the *pomp* and ceremony of the Olympics.

     A fanfare   **B** boredom   **C** brightness   **D** heat

_____ 6. Throwing the *javelin* was a part of a tough five-event contest.

     A stone   **B** spear   **C** arrow   **D** ball

_____ 7. Each *contestant* had to perform well in all five events in order to win.

     A winner   **B** participant   **C** observer   **D** official

_____ 8. Each athlete was very *competitive* because winning was extremely important.

     A interested   **B** exhausted   **C** deliberate   **D** aggressive

_____ 9. To win was the *supreme* achievement that all competitors wished for; to lose meant shame.

     A most annoying   **B** most frightening   **C** greatest   **D** lowest

_____ 10. The Olympic games meant so much to the people of ancient Greece that they would *proclaim* a truce during a time of war in order to hold the games.

     A destroy   **B** disturb   **C** declare   **D** defeat

Word Map

Words can be put on a kind of graphic organizer, or map, to show what they have in common. Use the vocabulary words in the box to complete the word map about both ancient and modern Olympic games. Add other words that you know to each group.

contestants	competitive	tribute
strenuous	stadium	javelin

Vocabulary in Context

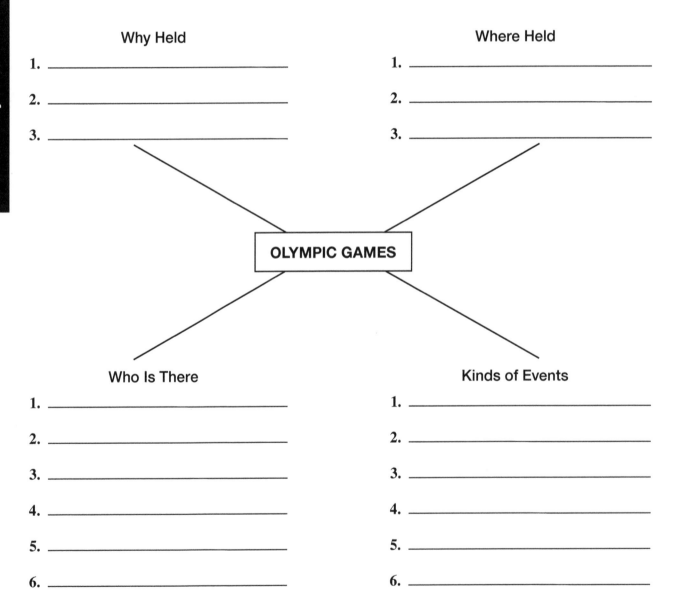

Why Held

1. _____

2. _____

3. _____

Where Held

1. _____

2. _____

3. _____

OLYMPIC GAMES

Who Is There

1. _____

2. _____

3. _____

4. _____

5. _____

6. _____

Kinds of Events

1. _____

2. _____

3. _____

4. _____

5. _____

6. _____

Connotations

Some words are very close in meaning, yet there are small differences among them. The words suggest slightly different things. This means that the words have different **connotations**. Words can have positive connotations and negative connotations. For example, read the two sentences below.

- My brother is very <u>thrifty</u> in his spending.
- My brother is very <u>cheap</u> in his spending.

Both *thrifty* and *cheap* mean "conservative," but *thrifty* has a positive connotation and *cheap* has a negative connotation.

Read the sentence pairs below. One of the sentences in each pair contains an underlined word with a positive connotation, and one contains an underlined word with a negative connotation. Write *positive* or *negative* on the lines next to the sentences.

1. _____   John is a very <u>competitive</u> player on the court.

   _____   John is a very <u>pushy</u> player on the court.

2. _____   We participated in <u>grueling</u> activities in gym class today.

   _____   We participated in <u>strenuous</u> activities in gym class today.

Find the Word

Read each sentence. Look for clues to help you complete each sentence with a word from the box. Write the word on the line.

pomp	tribute	stadium
javelin	proclaim	attendance

1. A ceremony that is very grand and elaborate would be filled with _____ and splendor.

2. The coach requires regular _____ at every practice; if a player misses a practice, she can't play in the game.

3. A _____ is a place where events are held.

4. People honor, or pay _____, to soldiers who have fought for their country.

5. I threw a spear, or a _____, at the sporting event.

Word Maze

All the words in the list below are hidden in the maze. The words are arranged forward, backward, up, down, and diagonally. Put a circle around each word as you find it and cross the word off the list. Different words may overlap and use the same letter.

pomp	tribute	stadium	strenuous	competitive
contestant	supreme	javelin	proclaim	attendance

Vocabulary in Context

```
R  T  W  E  C  T  R  I  B  U  T  E  X
L  M  N  U  M  Y  C  W  W  C  P  O  K
I  Y  C  A  S  K  O  O  G  E  Y  Y  B
Y  P  Q  S  T  U  M  G  Q  G  F  N  E
M  M  X  J  R  S  P  T  S  G  L  A  C
I  K  Q  A  A  U  E  R  Y  O  M  W  N
A  M  Q  V  D  O  T  T  E  L  M  T  A
L  U  N  E  C  U  I  G  N  M  G  Q  D
C  I  W  L  K  N  T  X  P  O  E  O  N
O  D  D  I  D  E  I  G  L  P  C  T  E
R  A  D  N  I  R  V  E  C  M  U  H  T
P  T  S  Z  Y  T  E  C  P  M  O  P  T
E  S  E  Q  E  S  O  L  B  R  L  Z  A
```

    Vocabulary in Context G6, SV 9780547625799

Name _____ Date _____

Analogies

An **analogy** compares two pairs of words. The relationship between the first pair of words is the same as the relationship between the second pair of words.

Example: *Heavy* is to *light* as *hot* is to *cold.*

Use the words in the box to complete the following analogies.

supreme	tribute	contestant	strenuous	javelin	proclaim

1. *Smallest* is to *least* as *highest* is to _____.

2. *Game* is to *player* as *contest* is to _____.

3. *Question* is to *ask* as *statement* is to _____.

4. *Swing* is to *bat* as *throw* is to _____.

5. *Mistreat* is to *insult* as *honor* is to _____.

6. *Inactive* is to *sluggish* as *difficult* is to _____.

Cloze Paragraph

Use the words in the box to complete the paragraph. Then reread the paragraph to be sure it makes sense.

strenuous	tribute	attendance	pomp	stadium	competitive

If you wanted to compete as an athlete in the Olympic games, you would have to go through

(1) _____ training. You would have to be very **(2)** _____

in order to win. Or you might just enjoy watching the Olympic games with all their splendor and

(3) _____. Just being in **(4)** _____ could be truly exciting.

I have never sat in an Olympic **(5)** _____, but I would like to someday. I hope to

attend as a **(6)** _____ to my grandfather, who competed in the Olympics in the

high jump competition.

Name _____ Date _____

Standardized Test Practice

Read each sentence. Circle the word that best completes the sentence.

 TIP
Before you choose an answer, try reading the sentences with each answer choice. This will help you choose an answer that makes sense.

1. The crowd was impressed by the _____ of the ceremony.

   A tickets   B heat   C pomp   D time

2. In her acceptance speech, the winner paid _____ to her acting coach.

   A tribute   B money   C energy   D dismissal

3. The judges will _____ the winners at the end of the competition.

   A send   B train   C ridicule   D proclaim

4. The _____ are at the starting line, ready to begin the race.

   A spectators   B contestants   C larger-than-life   D modern

5. Some of the races are very _____ and tiring.

   A strenuous   B humorous   C ancient   D supreme

6. The large _____ holds 50,000 spectators.

   A container   B stadium   C library   D magazine

7. The bad weather caused poor _____ at the events; most of the people chose to stay home.

   A seats   B friendship   C lights   D attendance

8. I am amazed at how far that competitor can throw the _____.

   A javelin   B monitor   C competition   D stadium

9. Winning the gold medal in the 400-meter relay was a _____ achievement for the girls on the team.

   A sudden   B supreme   C disappointing   D simple

10. Jamison is a _____ player who always wants to win.

    A competitive   B contestant   C illiterate   D visual

Understanding Related Words

The words in the box are closely related to the vocabulary words. See how many of the words you already know. Use the glossary to find the definitions of unfamiliar words.

candidate	attained	cross-country	gauge	archives
stopwatch	spectators	factor	capable	scoreboard

Write each word from the box in front of its meaning.

1. _____: a watch that can be instantly stopped and started, used for measuring tiny amounts of time

2. _____: people who watch something or look on without taking part

3. _____: to measure something; to judge

4. _____: a board on which scores of a sporting event are posted

5. _____: person who seeks a position of honor

6. _____: going across open country such as fields and woods instead of using a road

7. _____: element or idea that helps to bring about a result

8. _____: historical records

9. _____: able; having the power, ability, and fitness to do something

10. _____: reached, achieved; gained through effort

Word Skills

Challenge Yourself

1. Name two factors that are important to success in life.

_____

2. Name an activity that you are capable of doing well.

_____

Word Groups

Read each pair of words. Think about how they are alike. Write the word from the box that best completes each group.

spectators	gauge	stopwatch	candidate	capable	archives

1. records, documents, _____

2. audience, fans, _____

3. clock, timer, _____

4. able, ready, _____

5. applicant, nominee, _____

6. judge, measure, _____

Rewriting Sentences

Rewrite these sentences using one of the words from the box.

cross-country	attained	gauge	scoreboard	archives	factor

1. The rower achieved her goal of finishing the race.

_____

2. The coach will carefully determine the distance.

_____

3. Javier's love of animals was a major element in his decision to become a veterinarian.

_____

4. The board showing the score proved that we won the game by a narrow margin.

_____

5. Her name is in the school's historical records.

_____

6. Running across open fields is one way to train for many sports.

_____

Word Skills

Writing

In this selection, you learned that winning was everything to the athletes at the ancient Olympic games. Athletes who take part in today's Olympics believe that winning is important, but they also stress the importance of meeting new people, sharing new experiences, traveling to new places, and having the privilege of being able to compete.

If you were competing in the Olympics, what would be most important to you? Write a paragraph describing how you think you would feel if you were a competitor in the next Olympic games. What event would you compete in? What experiences would you hope to have? Use some vocabulary words from this unit in your writing.

_____

_____

_____

_____

_____

_____

_____

_____

_____

_____

Writing

Wall of Wonder

Read the selection. Think about the meanings of the **boldfaced** words. Then go back to the selection. Underline the words or sentences that give you a clue to the meaning of each **boldfaced** word.

Have you ever thought about the walls of your house as your own personal means of protection? They are. They protect you from the weather outside. More important, they let you decide who to let in and who to keep out of your house. Two thousand years ago, the Chinese people had the same idea. But they built a wall around their entire country!

The Great Wall of China was built at the command of China's first emperor. Before his reign, China was split into several warring states, each surrounded by its own wall. The emperor united these states. One way of showing their **unity** was to have one wall surrounding all of China.

The emperor claimed that the wall's purpose was **defensive**. It was intended to protect China from attacks by the fierce **nomads** who wandered the Gobi Desert, north of China. Also, it was a symbol of the emperor's power. He forced a million men to work on the wall. Many of them had been his enemies. For most, becoming a **laborer** was a death sentence. So many men died in building the Great Wall that it has been called "the longest cemetery in the world."

Later emperors built **extensions** onto the Great Wall to make it longer. Today it measures 3,700 miles along China's northern border. But the wall could not always protect the empire from **conquest**. The wandering warriors of the north swept across it numerous times to take over the country. Even though the wall didn't always successfully serve as a physical barrier, it did succeed as a unifying force for the country. The Chinese people came to think of everyone "inside the wall" as belonging together.

The Great Wall has **withstood** over two thousand years of harsh weather and invading armies. This **architectural** marvel winds like a snake across varied **terrains**, which include mountains, valleys, and rivers. It is one of the world's most **awesome** wonders.

Name _____ Date _____

Context Clues

For each sentence write the letter of the word that is closest in meaning to the word or words in italics. Use context clues to help you choose the correct answer.

_____ 1. The Great Wall of China has *endured* bad weather and invading armies.

       A described   **B** withstood   **C** ignored   **D** considered

_____ 2. China's first emperor ordered that the wall be built for *protective* measures.

       A descriptive   **B** confusing   **C** defensive   **D** conforming

_____ 3. Fierce *wanderers* of the Gobi Desert were at times stopped from attacking by the huge wall, but, in the end, they did sweep across it.

       A nomads   **B** strangers   **C** protectors   **D** citizens

_____ 4. The Great Wall of China did provide the people with a feeling of *belonging together*, of being a whole country instead of a group of warring states.

       A distance   **B** unity   **C** distress   **D** awareness

_____ 5. For anyone who was a *worker* on the wall, it could be a death sentence.

       A laborer   **B** student   **C** fighter   **D** judge

_____ 6. The varied *areas of land* upon which the wall was built made work very difficult.

       A designs   **B** materials   **C** cities   **D** terrains

_____ 7. Not only did many men die working on the original wall, but thousands more died building *added parts* ordered by later emperors.

       A entrances   **B** treatments   **C** covers   **D** extensions

_____ 8. No matter how many extensions were added, the wall did not prevent wandering warriors from achieving an occasional *victory*.

       A conquest   **B** concern   **C** defeat   **D** retreat

_____ 9. Although China has changed greatly, the *building* design of the Wall has barely changed.

       A attractive   **B** serious   **C** architectural   **D** material

_____ 10. The Great Wall of China is one of the most *magnificent* wonders of the world.

       A amusing   **B** disturbing   **C** discussed   **D** awesome

Name _____   Date _____

Word Map

Words can be put on a kind of graphic organizer, or map, to show what they have in common. Use the vocabulary words in the box to complete the word map about the Great Wall of China. Add other words that you know to each group.

conquests	withstood	terrains	nomads	unity
defensive	laborers	awesome	extensions	architectural

Why Built

1. _____ of country

2. _____ measures

3. _____

4. _____

How Built

1. millions of _____

2. across many different kinds of

_____

3. several _____

4. _____

GREAT WALL OF CHINA

After the Wall Was Built

1. _____ attacked

2. military _____

3. _____ weather

4. _____

Words That Describe It

1. _____ wonder

2. _____ marvel

3. _____

4. _____

Name _____ Date _____

Find the Word

Read each sentence. Look for clues to help you complete each sentence with the correct word from the box. Write the word on the line.

conquests	withstood	terrains	nomads	unity
defensive	laborers	awesome	extensions	architectural

1. The _____ design of the Great Wall of China was magnificent.

2. Building the Great Wall of China was an enormous task that required thousands of
_____.

3. Constructing the wall was made more difficult by the varied _____ on which it was built.

4. One reason the emperor had the wall built was to bring together the warring states within his kingdom and give them a sense of _____.

5. The emperor also built the wall as part of his _____ strategy to protect his people from invaders.

6. Some of the invaders were _____ who wandered the Gobi Desert north of China.

7. The wall was not always able to protect the Chinese people from invaders'
_____, however.

8. Over the years, other emperors had workers add _____ to the wall to make it longer.

9. This magnificent wall has _____ centuries of harsh weather and has survived numerous attacks by fierce invaders.

10. The Great Wall of China still stands as one of the world's _____ wonders.

Vocabulary in Context G6, SV 9780547625799

Vocabulary in Context

Crossword Puzzle

Use the clues and the words in the box to complete the crossword puzzle.

conquest	withstood	terrains	nomads	unity
defensive	laborers	awesome	extensions	architectural

Vocabulary in Context

Across

3. Workers
6. Parts that are added on to something
8. Different kinds of land
9. A sense of togetherness
10. Wanderers

Down

1. Having to do with designing and constructing buildings
2. Survived or held up to
4. Amazing or magnificent
5. Used for protection
7. The act of taking over by force

Analogies

An **analogy** compares two pairs of words. The relationship between the first pair of words is the same as the relationship between the second pair of words.

Example: *Sweet* is to *sour* as *dark* is to *light*.

Use the words in the box to complete the following analogies.

nomad	conquest	laborer	awesome	unity

1. *Player* is to *competitor* as *wanderer* is to _____.

2. *Liquid* is to *solid* as *separation* is to _____.

3. *Vacation* is to *holiday* as *invasion* is to _____.

4. *Car* is to *automobile* as *worker* is to _____.

5. *Stroll* is to *sprint* as *unimpressive* is to _____.

Cloze Paragraph

Use the words in the box to complete the paragraph. Then reread the paragraph to be sure it makes sense.

withstood	laborer	unity	architectural

To build the Great Wall, people needed to work together in **(1)** _____. Every

(2) _____ who worked on the wall was skilled, and many different materials were

used. As a result, the Great Wall has endured thousands of years of bad weather and has

(3) _____ the attacks of invading armies. Its **(4)** _____

design is so solid that it will most likely last forever.

Name _____ Date _____

Standardized Test Practice

Read the phrase. Look for the word or words that have the same or almost the same meaning as the boldfaced word. Circle the letter for your choice.

TIP

Always read all the answer choices. Many choices may make sense. Only one answer choice has the same or almost the same meaning as the boldfaced word.

1. tired **laborer**
   A nomad   B warrior   C worker   D rider

2. **architectural** design
   A defensive   B building   C popular   D awesome

3. wall **extensions**
   A rocky terrains B added parts   C long directions D strong materials

4. **defensive** measures
   A simple   B awesome   C dull   D protective

5. rough **terrains**
   A areas of land B thunderstorms   C bodies of water D materials

6. feeling of **unity**
   A confusion   B victory   C sadness   D togetherness

7. **withstood** attacks
   A lost   B endured   C ignored   D understood

8. army's **conquest**
   A defense   B victory   C uniform   D unity

9. **awesome** sight
   A huge   B forgotten   C ordinary   D magnificent

10. fierce **nomads**
    A dogs   B wanderers   C emperors   D walls

Name _____ Date _____

Using Context

The words in the box are also related to wonders that amaze us; in this case, burial places for Egyptian kings. See how many of the words you already know. Use the glossary to find the definitions of unfamiliar words.

pharaoh	burial	archaeology	incline	mummy
elevated	triangular	spiritual	tedious	diagonal

Read each sentence, paying attention to the meaning of the underlined word. Write a definition for the word as it is used in the sentence.

1. The method of burial for many people who have died is to place them in a grave marked with a stone.

   Burial means _____.

2. The grave of an Egyptian king, or pharaoh, was marked by a pyramid built with stones.

   Pharaoh means _____.

3. The pharaoh's body was wrapped in layers of cloth, and the mummy was placed in a secret room inside the pyramid.

   Mummy means _____.

4. The Egyptian pyramids are amazing structures because the huge stone blocks were elevated on ramps without the use of machines.

   Elevated means _____.

5. Imagine how steep the incline of the ramps had to be to raise the stones to such great heights.

   Incline means _____.

6. Students of archaeology believe it was farmers who built the pyramids.

   Archaeology means _____.

7. Some historians say 50 years was not an unusual amount of time spent to build the huge pyramids with three-sided, or triangular, sides.

   Triangular means _____.

8. Most workers spent their lives and strength doing the tedious job of building the pyramids.

   Tedious means _____.

9. The pyramids' diagonal sides, which slant downward, may have been designed to imitate the sun's slanting rays.

   Diagonal means _____.

10. It is thought that the triangular shape of the pyramids' sides had spiritual meaning for the Egyptians in that the shape would somehow help the pharaoh reach heaven.

    Spiritual means _____.

Word Skills

Unit 10
Vocabulary in Context G6, SV 9780547625799

Word Sense

Read each phrase. Check a dictionary to see if the words make sense together. If they do, write *yes* on the line. If they do not, write *no* and write a new word that does make sense with the underlined word.

1. <u>tedious</u> work _____

2. <u>triangular</u> pencil _____

3. Roman <u>pharaoh</u> _____

4. <u>diagonal</u> sides _____

5. <u>burial</u> room _____

6. fat <u>incline</u> _____

7. songs of <u>archaeology</u> _____

8. blocks <u>elevated</u> _____

9. <u>mummy</u> talked _____

10. <u>spiritual</u> ramp _____

Understanding Multiple-Meaning Words

The words in the box have more than one meaning. Look for clues in each sentence to tell which meaning is being used. Write the letter of the meaning next to the correct sentence.

incline	elevated	spiritual
a. a sloping surface	a. raised or lifted up	a. relating to the spirit or soul
b. to bend or bow	b. improved the mind or emotions	b. a religious song

_____ 1. The people <u>incline</u> their heads to the king.

_____ 2. The car got stuck going up the icy <u>incline</u>.

_____ 3. The stone blocks were <u>elevated</u> by ropes.

_____ 4. The speech <u>elevated</u> the audience's mood.

_____ 5. Everyone joined together to sing the <u>spiritual</u>.

_____ 6. Some people believe that shapes of things have <u>spiritual</u> meanings.

Writing

The Great Wall of China has been a popular tourist site for many years. One section most often visited by tourists is the Badaling Pass. Another is the Shanhaiguan Gate, on the far eastern section of the wall.

Imagine that you have been hired to create an advertisement to persuade more people to visit the Great Wall. Use facts from the story to help you stir up excitement about the wall. Be sure to use colorful, vivid words to persuade people to plan a trip. Use some vocabulary words from this unit in your writing.

_____

_____

_____

_____

_____

_____

_____

_____

_____

_____

_____

_____

_____

Writing

Glossary

A

abandon	*verb*	to leave; to give up something (page 84)
advantageous	*adjective*	helping or putting ahead; favorable (page 15)
amateurs	*noun*	people who are inexperienced or not professional (page 48)
anticipation	*noun*	hope; looking forward to or expecting something (page 58)
archaeology	*noun*	the science that studies objects from the past (page 105)
architectural	*adjective*	having to do with designing or constructing buildings (page 98)
archives	*noun*	records (page 95)
assault	*noun*	a sudden attack, either verbal or physical (page 8)
assisted	*verb*	helped (page 78)
associate	*verb; noun*	(v.) to connect in thought; join with another (n.) companion, partner, or friend (page 24)
assurance	*noun*	a statement intended to make a person sure or certain (page 24)
assured	*verb*	told positively; made someone sure of something (page 18)
attained	*verb*	to gain through effort (page 95)
attendance	*noun*	the number of people who come to an event (page 88)
awesome	*adjective*	causing wonder or amazement (page 98)

B

beheld	*verb*	looked at; saw (page 78)
benefactor	*noun*	a person who gives help (page 26)
beneficent	*adjective*	showing kindness or doing good for others (page 26)
beneficial	*adjective*	healthy or good for someone or something; favorable or causing a good result (page 24)
beneficiary	*noun*	a person who receives help (page 26)
benefit	*verb; noun*	to receive good from (v.); anything that is good for a person or thing (n.); an event in which the profits are donated to a cause (n.) (pages 19, 68, 74)
bifocal	*adjective*	having lenses that allow for both close-up and faraway vision (page 68)
brilliance	*noun*	the quality or condition of being bright (page 35)
brilliant	*adjective*	shining brightly; having great abilities (page 28)
burial	*noun*	the placing of a dead body in a grave (page 105)
bust	*noun*	sculpture of a person's head and shoulders (page 78)

C

calculated	*verb*	figured out by analyzing or using a mathematical process (page 38)
candidate	*noun*	one who seeks an office or honor (page 95)

capable	*adjective*	able (page 95)
carvings	*noun*	pieces of art made by cutting stone or wood (page 78)
claimed	*verb*	called for or required (page 18)
classic	*adjective*	remarkable; of the highest standards (page 45)
classified	*verb*	categorized or arranged in a group or class (page 38)
collapses	*verb*	falls down or falls to pieces; caves in (page 38)
collided	*verb*	crashed violently against each other (page 9)
collision	*noun*	occurs when two or more objects collide, or strike against each other (page 15)
companion	*noun*	one who often goes along with or accompanies another (page 84)
competitive	*adjective*	driven by the desire to win or succeed (page 88)
completion	*noun*	a finishing; process of completing (page 8)
comprehend	*verb*	to understand (page 68)
concentrate	*verb; noun*	to bring together in one place (v.); to give careful attention to (v.); a substance that is especially strong (n.) (pages 38, 44)
concentration	*noun*	the action of focusing one's attention on a task or subject (page 45)
conditions	*noun*	the state in which a person or thing is (page 18)
conduct	*verb*	to guide or lead (page 64)
confer	*verb*	join together to discuss (page 35)
conference	*noun*	a group joined together for discussion (page 28)
conquest	*noun*	the act of taking over by force (page 98)
contestant	*noun*	a person who takes part in a contest (page 88)
contracts	*verb; noun*	agreements (n.); draws together (v.); gets or acquires (v.) (pages 38, 44)
contributions	*noun*	donations or payments to a cause (pages 18, 68)
core	*noun*	the central or most important part (page 38)
craze	*noun*	madness; an enthusiasm shared by many people (page 58)
creates	*verb*	makes a thing that has not been made before (page 38)
crisis	*noun*	a time of great difficulty or danger (page 64)
cross-country	*adjective*	moving across open country (page 95)

D

decrease	*verb*	to grow smaller in size, amount, or intensity (page 24)
defensive	*adjective*	used for protection (page 98)
demand	*verb*	to ask for as a right (page 49)
demanding	*adjective*	insisting on one's way (page 55)
demolished	*verb*	torn down or smashed into pieces; destroyed (page 8)
demolition	*noun*	the action of destroying or demolishing something (page 15)

design	*verb*	to plan the look and/or function of something; (page 45)
destination	*noun*	place to which a person or thing is going or being sent (page 28)
destiny	*noun*	someone or something's future or fate (page 35)
developed	*verb*	worked out in detail; grown (page 38)
diagonal	*adjective*	slanted; going up and down at an angle (page 105)
disadvantage	*noun*	unfavorable condition or circumstance (page 8)
disappeared	*verb*	was no longer in view; was unable to be seen (page 16)
disapproved	*verb*	refused to agree with or approve (page 16)
disband	*verb*	to break apart or separate (page 15)
discomfort	*noun*	an unpleasant condition (page 16)
discouraged	*adjective*	depressed; not hopeful (page 28)
discouragement	*noun*	a loss of confidence or enthusiasm (page 35)
dislike	*verb*	to view something in a negative way (page 16)
disorderly	*adjective*	not in a neat or orderly state (page 15)
dispossess	*verb*	to take away or deprive someone of something (page 35)
dissolve	*verb*	melt from solid to liquid form (page 15)
distrust	*verb*	to not believe in someone's honesty (page 16)
distrusted	*verb*	had no trust in; was suspicious of (page 58)
distrustful	*adjective*	having no trust in; suspicious of (page 64)
dramatic	*adjective*	exciting; theatrical (page 78)
dynamite	*noun*	a mixture that blows up with great force; an explosive (page 58)
dynamiter	*noun*	a person who works with explosives (page 64)

E

effect	*noun*	something that happens as a result of something else (page 15)
effective	*adjective*	producing the desired result; making a striking impression (page 8)
effortless	*adjective*	easy and without effort; requiring no energy or work (page 24)
efforts	*noun*	uses of energy to do something; strong attempts (page 18)
elevated	*verb*	raised; lifted (page 105)
empty-handed	*adjective*	with nothing to show for one's efforts (page 58)
encourage	*verb*	to give hope or support to someone (page 35)
epidemic	*noun*	a sickness that spreads quickly (page 58)
established	*verb*	started; created or set up (page 68)
estimate	*noun*	judgment or careful guess about amount, size, or value (page 8)
exaggerate	*verb*	to make something seem larger, better, greater, or worse than it really is (page 46)
examine	*verb*	to look closely at something (page 46)

exception	*noun*	something that is different from the rest; something that does not follow the rules (page 45)
exceptional	*adjective*	unusual; out of the ordinary (page 38)
excess	*adjective*	more than usual or necessary (page 46)
exit	*noun*	a way out of a location (page 45)
expand	*verb*	to spread out; make larger (page 38)
experience	*noun*	knowledge gained by doing or seeing things (page 84)
exploit	*noun*	a remarkable act; a bold deed (page 46)
exploration	*noun*	the action of traveling in an unfamiliar territory to discover new things (page 45)
explore	*verb*	to travel for the purpose of discovery; examine (page 38)
express	*verb*	to put into words (page 18)
expression	*noun*	a saying; the look on someone's face (page 24)
extensions	*noun*	pieces that are added on to something else (page 98)
exterior	*noun*	the outer surface or structure of something (page 45)
extinguish	*verb*	to put an end to; to cause to stop burning (page 45)
extraordinary	*adjective*	very unusual or remarkable (page 46)
extreme	*adjective*	much more than usual; something more than usual (page 38)

F

factor	*noun*	something that helps bring about a result (page 95)
founder	*noun*	the person who starts something (page 68)
fragment	*noun*	a part of something that has been broken off (page 64)

G

gauge	*verb*	to measure carefully; to determine the amount or distance (page 95)
gravity	*noun*	the natural force that pulls objects toward the center of Earth; heaviness, weight (page 38)

H

homesickness	*noun*	a deep longing for home (page 58)
homesteads	*noun*	houses, other buildings, and the land around them (page 58)

I

illustrate	*verb*	to make clear; to prove (pages 68, 74)
immediate	*adjective*	without delay; closest; nearest; instant (page 19)
incline	*noun*	slope; slanted surface (page 105)
increased	*verb*	became greater in size, number, power, etc. (page 19)
indebted	*adjective*	owing money or gratitude; obliged (page 29)
individual	*adjective*	particular; of, for, or by one person (page 48)

individualism	noun	a focus on being independent or self-reliant (page 55)
ineffective	adjective	not successful in achieving the desired result (page 15)
inscription	noun	words carved or written on something (page 78)
intellectual	adjective	having great mental capabilities (page 68)
interrupt	verb	to break in upon; hinder; stop (page 84)
invade	verb	to attack or enter by force (page 15)
invaders'	possessive noun	belonging to people who enter by force (page 8)
invasion	noun	an unwelcome intrusion or entry into a location (page 15)
issues	noun	matters of concern (page 18)

J

javelin	noun	a spear thrown in sporting contests (page 88)
jointly	adverb	together; in common (page 28)

L

laborer	noun	worker (page 98)
lacked	verb	was deficient in or completely without (page 28)
local	adjective	of or confined to a particular place (page 48)
locality	noun	a specific location nearby (page 55)
ludicrous	adjective	crazy or foolish (page 68)

M

majestic	adjective	impressive; grand or noble-looking (page 78)
meaningful	adjective	full of meaning; having significance (page 64)
mercy	noun	kindness; milder punishment (page 38)
metaphor	noun	comparison of two things by stating that one thing is another thing (page 30)
mishap	noun	an unlucky accident (page 8)
mission	noun	a special purpose or errand (page 8)
mummy	noun	a body that is preserved after death (page 105)

N

navigate	verb	to determine where you are and where you need to go in a ship, car, or airplane (page 15)
navigator	noun	one who steers or plots the course for a craft (page 9)
nomads	noun	wanderers (page 98)

O

occasionally	adverb	occuring infrequently or irregularly (page 55)
occasions	noun	particular times; special events (page 49)
office	noun	a room or a building used for a business (page 55)

officer	*noun*	a person who commands others (page 48)
opinion	*noun*	what one thinks (page 28)
opponent	*noun*	a competitor; one who competes with another (page 24)
opposed	*verb*	was against; tried to hinder (page 18)

P

parallel	*adverb*	extending in the same direction and being the same distance apart (page 48)
participate	*verb*	to take part in (page 18)
participation	*noun*	the act of taking part in an event or activity or cause (page 24)
patent	*verb*	to obtain government protection for an invention; to obtain a copyright (page 68)
personification	*noun*	figure of speech in which an object is given human attributes (page 30)
persuade	*verb*	to win over to do or believe (page 84)
pharaoh	*noun*	a king of ancient Egypt (page 105)
plunged	*verb*	dove down or thrusted with force (page 28)
pomp	*noun*	splendid or showy display (page 88)
possess	*verb*	to own or have (page 28)
predicted	*verb*	foretold; told of an event beforehand (page 84)
prediction	*noun*	something a person claims will happen in the future (page 68)
prefer	*verb*	to like better (page 28)
preference	*noun*	a liking of one thing over another (page 35)
process	*noun*	a set of actions or changes in a particular order (page 64)
proclaim	*verb*	to declare publicly (page 88)
produced	*verb*	brought about or caused (page 38)
profound	*adjective*	showing great thought; deeply felt (page 46)
progress	*noun*	movement in a forward direction toward a destination; growth; development; improvement; movement forward (pages 45 and 84)
progressive	*adjective*	new and different; developing or advancing in seriousness; forward thinking (pages 68, 74)
prolong	*verb*	to cause to last longer (page 46)
prompt	*adjective*	on time (page 19)
propel	*verb*	to push; to make go forward (page 46)
protest	*verb*	to speak out against (page 46)
provoke	*verb*	to make angry (page 46)
pursue	*verb*	to follow in order to catch (page 84)

R

realization	*noun*	the act of becoming aware of something (page 15)
realize	*verb*	to understand clearly; achieve (page 8)
remarkable	*adjective*	unusual; worthy of notice (page 84)
renowned	*adjective*	very famous (page 78)
resident	*noun*	a person living in a place (page 64)
results	*noun*	that which happens because of something; good or useful effect (page 19)
right	*noun*	a just claim (page 48)

S

scoreboard	*noun*	a large board that shows scores and times in athletic contests (page 95)
screech	*noun*	a shrill scream or cry (page 48)
sculptor	*noun*	an artist who creates figures from stone, wood, or clay (page 78)
section	*noun*	any distinct or separate part (page 49)
segment	*noun*	a piece or a part of (page 28)
severe	*adjective*	serious; very strict; harsh; dangerous (page 9)
shanties	*noun*	roughly built, run-down shacks (page 58)
shatter	*verb*	to break into pieces; destroy (page 49)
significant	*adjective*	important; of great weight or value (page 68)
simile	*noun*	comparison of two things using the words *like* or *as* (page 30)
site	*noun*	a position or place (page 84)
skeptical	*adjective*	disbelieving or doubtful (page 68)
sociable	*adjective*	outgoing; friendly; eager to participate in social occasions (page 24)
socialize	*verb*	to interact with other people (page 26)
society	*noun*	a group of persons joined together for a common purpose; human beings living together as a group (page 18)
sociology	*noun*	the study of human society (page 24)
solitary	*adjective*	without other people (page 58)
spectators	*noun*	people who watch something; viewers (page 95)
spiritual	*adjective*	religious; sacred (page 105)
stadium	*noun*	an enclosed area used for sporting and other events (page 88)
stopwatch	*noun*	a watch used to time speeds in contests (page 95)
strategy	*noun*	skillful planning of anything (page 64)
strenuous	*adjective*	requiring great effort (page 88)
sufficient	*adjective*	as much as is needed; enough (page 64)
summit	*noun*	the highest part; top (page 78)

supremacy	*noun*	highest in authority or power (page 55)
supreme	*adjective*	highest in degree; greatest (pages 48, 88)
suspect	*verb; noun*	to think it likely or guess (v.); to believe to be guilty of something (v.); a person who is considered guilty (n.) (pages 29, 36)
suspicion	*noun*	a belief in the guilt of someone or something (page 35)

T

technical	*adjective*	having to do with applied or technical sciences (page 55)
technicality	*noun*	a point of law or small detail (page 55)
technician	*noun*	a person who applies technical knowledge or skill (page 55)
technique	*noun*	method or level of skill (page 49)
technocracy	*noun*	a government or society run by technology experts (page 56)
technology	*noun*	a branch of science dealing with engineering or applied sciences (page 55)
tedious	*adjective*	slow and boring (page 105)
terrains	*noun*	certain areas of land (page 98)
transfer	*verb*	to move or change from one place to another (page 35)
transformed	*verb*	changed in form or appearance (page 29)
transmit	*verb*	to pass something along; broadcast (page 35)
triangular	*adjective*	having a three-sided shape (page 105)
tribute	*noun*	something done or given to show respect or to honor (page 88)
twilight	*noun*	the period of time from sunset to dark (page 8)

U

unity	*noun*	the state of being whole; togetherness (page 98)
urgent	*adjective*	demanding immediate attention (page 28)

V

vessel	*noun*	a ship or large boat (page 48)
vicinity	*noun*	the region near or about a place; closeness (page 8)
visionary	*noun*	a person who has insight or imagination into the future (page 68)

W

withstood	*verb*	resisted; survived; endured (page 98)

Y

yarns	*noun*	tales or stories (page 48)

Vocabulary in Context G6, SV 9780547625799

Answer Key

Pages 10–11

1. D
2. B
3. B
4. C
5. B
6. A
7. B
8. D
9. B
10. D
11. D
12. D
13. A
14. C
15. B

Page 12

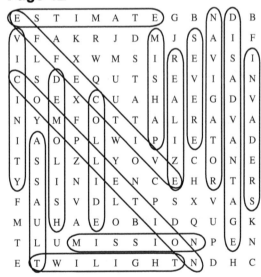

Page 13

1. C
2. D
3. D
4. B
5. C
6. D

7. B
8. D
9. B
10. D

Page 14

1. different
2. same
3. different
4. different
5. same

Page 15

1. A
2. B
3. C
4. A
5. A

Page 16

1. not in a neat or orderly state
2. an unpleasant condition
3. to break apart; to separate
4. melted from solid to liquid form
5. refused to agree with or approve of
6. to not believe in someone's honesty
7. was no longer in view; was unable to be seen
8. to view something in a negative way

Page 17

Answers will vary.

Pages 20–21

1. A
2. B
3. A
4. C
5. D
6. A
7. C

Vocabulary in Context G6, SV 9780547625799

8. A

9. A

10. A

11. C

12. D

13. C

14. C

15. A

Page 22

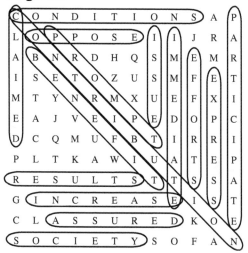

Page 23

1. D

2. C

3. A

4. B

5. D

6. C

7. B

8. B

9. D

10. D

11. A

12. C

Page 24

1. beneficial

2. decrease

3. opponent

4. sociable

5. effortless

6. assurance

7. expression

8. associate

9. sociology

10. participation

Page 25
Understanding Multiple-Meaning Words

1. c

2. b

3. b

4. a

5. c

True or False

1. F

2. T

3. T

4. T

5. F

6. F

7. F

8. F

9. T

10. T

Page 26
The Latin Roots *socius* and *bene*

1. e

2. b

3. a

4. d

5. c

6. d

7. e

8. b

9. c

10. a

Dictionary Skills

1. effortless;easy and without effort

2. expression; a saying

3. opponent; a competitor

4. sociable; outgoing

5. sociology; the study of human society

Page 27

Answers will vary.

Page 30

1. A

2. C

3. B

4. C

Pages 31–32

1. D

2. C

3. B

4. B

5. B

6. C

7. C

8. B

9. B

10. A

11. A

12. B

13. D

14. B

15. B

Page 33

Across

1. destination

8. ton

9. net

10. st

12. PTA

14. CD

15. conference

20. opinions

21. do

22. USA

24. she

25. oar

27. AMA

29. urgent

31. rah

32. fi

33. suspect

37. ah

39. area

40. segment

Down

1. discourage

2. st

3. to

4. in

5. transforms

6. once

7. Ned

11. tops

12. pro

13. ten

16. Nia

17. fn

18. eighth

19. joint

23. prefers

26. ag

28. art

30. nice

34. Pa

35. tap

36. me

37. AM

38. he

Page 34

1. C

2. A

3. E

4. B
5. B
6. E
7. A
8. B
9. C
10. E

Page 35
Synonyms and Antonyms
1. S
2. A
3. S
4. A
5. S
6. A
7. A
8. S
9. A
10. S

Dictionary Skills
1. Answers will vary.
2. after
3. noun
4. three
5. act of favoring one above another

Page 36
Understanding Multiple-Meaning Words
1. c
2. b
3. b
4. a
5. b

Word Meaning
1. C
2. A
3. B
4. C

Page 37
Answers will vary.

Pages 40–41
1. D
2. A
3. C
4. A
5. A
6. D
7. B
8. B
9. C
10. B
11. C
12. B
13. D
14. D
15. A

Page 42
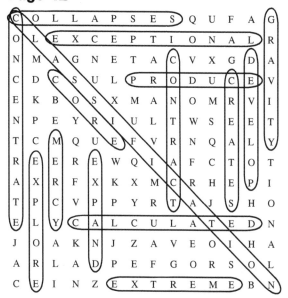

Page 43
1. D
2. A
3. A
4. D
5. C

6. A

7. A

8. C

9. A

10. B

Page 44

1. a
2. b
3. a
4. b
5. c
6. b
7. a
8. a
9. c
10. b

Page 45

1. decrease
2. exploration
3. progress
4. exterior
5. classic
6. exit
7. concentration
8. exception
9. extinguish
10. design

Page 46

1. exploit
2. examine
3. exaggerate
4. extraordinary
5. excess
6. provoke
7. propel
8. prolong
9. protest
10. profound

Page 47

Answers will vary.

Pages 50–51

1. C
2. A
3. B
4. B
5. C
6. C
7. A
8. D
9. A
10. D
11. B
12. D
13. B
14. A
15. B

Page 52

Across

1. section
3. yarn
5. right
8. VP
10. ate
11. AI
12. sw
13. catch
16. calm
17. or
18. in
19. all
21. supreme
23. ion
24. umps
26. shatters
27. Dad

Down

1. screech

2. NJ
3. yet
4. rr
6. go
7. technique
8. vessel
9. parallel
14. tar
15. amateur
17. oh
20. fits
22. used
25. he

Page 53
1. B
2. D
3. B
4. D
5. A
6. C
7. A
8. B
9. D
10. C

Page 54
1. b
2. e
3. c
4. d
5. a
6. c
7. b
8. a
9. c
10. a

Page 55
1. locality
2. office
3. occasionally
4. demanding
5. supremacy
6. technician
7. technicality
8. individualism
9. technology
10. technical

Page 56
1. technical
2. technocracy
3. technology
4. technician
5. technicality
6. technicality
7. technician
8. technocracy
9. technology
10. technical

Page 57
Answers will vary.

Page 59
Context Clues
1. epidemic
2. anticipation
3. craze
4. dynamite
5. shanties
6. solitary
7. distrusted
8. empty-handed
9. homesickness
10. homesteads

Word Groups
1. craze
2. dynamite
3. shanties
4. anticipation

Page 60
Word Origins
1. solitary
2. dynamite
3. homestead
4. epidemic
5. anticipation
6. distrust

Cloze Paragraph
1. craze
2. anticipation
3. shanties
4. solitary
5. homesickness
6. distrusted
7. empty-handed

Page 61
1. craze
2. distrusted
3. epidemic
4. anticipation
5. dynamite
6. solitary
7. homesickness
8. homesteads
9. shanties
10. empty-handed

Answer: a scanty shanty

Page 62
Sentences will vary. Accept reasonable responses.
1. no; A craze usually lasts a short time.
2. no; Shanties are shacks that provide short-term shelter.
3. yes
4. no; If you use dynamite, you are blowing something up.
5. yes
6. yes

7. no; If your family lives far away, you are likely to suffer from homesickness.
8. no; You feel a sense of anticipation about something that is going to happen.
9. no; A person with no friends leads a solitary life.
10. no; An epidemic is a quickly-spreading illness.

Page 63
1. C
2. B
3. C
4. D
5. A
6. B
7. A
8. B
9. D
10. C

Page 64
1. F
2. F
3. T
4. F
5. T
6. T
7. F
8. T
9. F
10. T

Sentences will vary. Accept reasonable responses.

Page 65
Answers will vary. Accept reasonable responses.

Page 66
Suffix *-ful*
Sentences will vary. Accept reasonable responses.

1. meaningful
2. painful
3. wonderful
4. helpful
5. forgetful

Latin Root *-duct*

1. induct
2. product
3. abduct
4. introduction
5. deduct

Page 67

Answers will vary.

Page 69

1. comprehend
2. skeptical
3. ludicrous
4. patent
5. progressive
6. bifocal
7. significant
8. established
9. benefit
10. prediction
11. founder
12. intellectual

Page 70

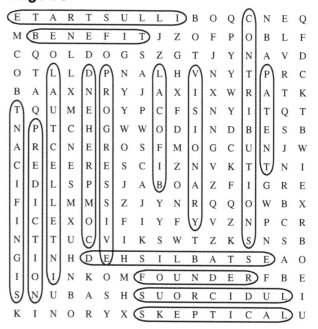

Page 71

1. comprehend
2. ludicrous
3. skeptical
4. significant
5. illustrate
6. prediction
7. benefit
8. established
9. bifocal
10. founder
11. intellectual
12. progressive
13. patent
14. visionary
15. contributions

Pages 72–73

1. B
2. B
3. A
4. D
5. B
6. B
7. A

Vocabulary in Context G6, SV 9780547625799

8. B
9. C
10. D
11. D
12. B
13. A
14. B
15. B

Page 74

1. b
2. a
3. a
4. b
5. b
6. a
7. a
8. b

Page 75

1. B
2. A
3. C
4. D
5. A
6. C
7. B
8. B
9. A
10. A
11. A
12. B

Page 76
The Suffix -ion

1. i
2. j
3. h
4. a
5. c
6. b
7. f

8. d
9. e
10. g

Word Pairs

Answers will vary. Sample answers are provided.

1. Nick is such a skeptic; he does not believe anything if he does not see it with his own eyes.
   Nick is skeptical that the reporter is telling the truth.
2. To learn spelling or math, you must use your intellect.
   Thinking is an intellectual process.
3. The way that a pump works is used to illustrate how the heart sends blood around the body.
   Her illustration of how the heart pumps blood taught us a lot.

Page 77

Answers will vary.

Page 79

1. carvings
2. bust
3. renowned
4. majestic
5. summit
6. sculptor
7. beheld
8. inscription
9. dramatic
10. assisted

Page 80
Word Groups

1. summit
2. renowned
3. beheld
4. majestic
5. dramatic

6. bust

Analogies

1. carvings
2. inscription
3. sculptor
4. bust
5. summit
6. renowned

Page 81
Across

2. majestic
8. assisted
9. inscription
10. dramatic

Down

1. beheld
3. carvings
4. sculptor
5. bust
6. renowned
7. summit

Page 82

Sentences will vary. Accept reasonable responses. Sample answers are provided.

1. no; A sculptor is known for his sculptures.
2. no; A dramatic performance excites the audience.
3. no; A bust shows the head and shoulders.
4. yes
5. no; An inscription is usually writing.
6. no; If you beheld a rainbow, you saw it.
7. yes
8. no; You would describe something majestic as grand and impressive.
9. no; If someone assisted you, they helped you.
10. yes

Page 83

1. C
2. D
3. B
4. A
5. C
6. A
7. B
8. C
9. D
10. B

Page 84

1. T
2. T
3. T
4. T
5. T
6. F
7. T
8. F
9. F
10. F

Sentences will vary. Accept reasonable responses.

Page 85

1. B
2. A
3. B
4. C
5. A
6. B
7. D
8. C
9. D
10. C

Page 86

1. protect
2. proceed
3. provide

4. profess

5. promote

6. profess

7. proceed

8. promote

Page 87

Answers will vary. Students should follow the poem format.

Page 89

1. A

2. B

3. C

4. D

5. A

6. B

7. B

8. D

9. C

10. C

Page 90

Additional words will vary.

Why Held: tribute

Where Held: stadium

Who Is There: contestants

Kinds of Events: javelin, competitive, strenuous

Page 91
Connotations

1. positive

   negative

2. negative

   positive

Find the Word

1. pomp

2. attendance

3. stadium

4. tribute

5. javelin

Page 92

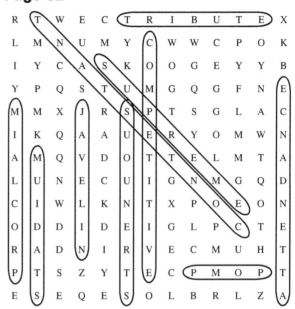

Page 93
Analogies

1. supreme

2. contestant

3. proclaim

4. javelin

5. tribute

6. strenuous

Cloze Paragraph

1. strenuous

2. competitive

3. pomp

4. attendance

5. stadium

6. tribute

Page 94

1. C

2. A

3. D

4. B

5. A

6. B

7. D

8. A

Vocabulary in Context G6, SV 9780547625799

9. B

10. A

Page 95
Understanding Related Words
1. stopwatch

2. spectators

3. gauge

4. scoreboard

5. candidate

6. cross-country

7. factor

8. archives

9. capable

10. attained

Challenge Yourself
Answers will vary. Sample responses are provided.

1. studying hard, listening well

2. playing piano, playing baseball

Page 96
Word Groups
1. archives

2. spectators

3. stopwatch

4. capable

5. candidate

6. gauge

Rewriting Sentences
1. The rower attained her goal of finishing the race.

2. The coach will gauge the distance.

3. Javier's love of animals was a factor in his decision to become a veterinarian.

4. The scoreboard proved that we won the game by a narrow margin.

5. Her name is in the school's archives.

6. Cross-country running is one way to train for many sports.

Page 97
Answers will vary.

Page 99
1. B

2. C

3. A

4. B

5. A

6. D

7. D

8. A

9. C

10. D

Page 100
Why Built

1. unity of country

2. defensive measures

Additional answers will vary.

How Built

1. millions of laborers

2. across many different kinds of terrains

3. several extensions

Additional answers will vary.

After the Wall Was Built

1. nomads attacked

2. military conquests

3. withstood weather

Additional answers will vary.

Words That Describe It

1. awesome wonder

2. architectural marvel

Additional answers will vary.

Page 101
1. architectural

2. laborers

3. terrains

4. unity

5. defensive
6. nomads
7. conquests
8. extensions
9. withstood
10. awesome

Page 102
Across
3. laborers
6. extensions
8. terrains
9. unity
10. nomads

Down
1. architectural
2. withstood
4. awesome
5. defensive
7. conquest

Page 103
Analogies
1. nomad
2. unity
3. conquest
4. laborer
5. awesome

Cloze Paragraph
1. unity
2. laborer
3. withstood
4. architectural

Page 104
1. C
2. B
3. B
4. D
5. A
6. D

7. B
8. B
9. D
10. B

Page 105
1. the placing of a dead body in a grave
2. a king of ancient Egypt
3. a body that is preserved after death
4. raised; lifted
5. slope; slanted surface
6. the science that studies objects from the past
7. having a three-sided shape
8. slow and boring
9. slanted; going up and down at an angle
10. religious; sacred

Page 106
Word Sense
Responses for *no* will vary. Suggested responses are provided.
1. yes
2. no, triangular shape
3. no, Egyptian pharaoh
4. yes
5. yes
6. no, steep incline
7. no, objects of archaeology
8. yes
9. no, mummy buried
10. no, spiritual meaning

Understanding Multiple-Meaning Words
1. b
2. a
3. a
4. b
5. b
6. a

Page 107
Answers will vary.

Printed in the USA
CPSIA information can be obtained
at www.ICGtesting.com
LVHW081358220124
769411LV00143B/1743